Dear Karen & [...]
   "Nurture their feelings
Protect their bodies
Embrace their souls.
                    Linda Brady

Dear Karen & Ross,
    May the unconditional love of
animals teach us to love ourselves
and others unconditionally!!
                    Joe Landis

NO MORE GOODBYES

Let us honor our heart and
soul connection to our
beloved pets!

Linda M. Brady

Reader's Comments

Linda Brady has dedicated many years of her life to helping people discover and understand the purpose and meaning of their lives. And now, with her second book, *NO MORE GOODBYES - A True Story* readers are allowed to experience the journey that brought her to this place of insight and devotion. This story reveals that her deep commitment to human life has, at its core, a spiritual connection to the animal world, specifically to her beloved dogs, which turn out to be guide dogs in the quest of her spiritual mission.

In telling "her story," Linda exposes the frailties and emotions of human struggle and self doubt that most people face in the journey of life. However, in writing her story, she brings the comfort of hope for all living beings. Linda Brady helped me identify the importance of a little dog, named Duski, that came into my life after my seventeen-year-old son's suicide in 1977. And now I've learned of the importance of the dogs in her life. Anyone who has ever had a special pet, and felt the power of their connection, will read this book with soul-searching interest.

Susan White-Bowden

Former TV reporter and anchor, author of six books, including EVERYTHING TO LIVE FOR, about her son Jody's suicide and her newest book RETURNING: Duski's Story to be released in 2004.

NO MORE GOODBYES

A True Story

Linda M. Brady

J. C. Landis

Marty Humphreys

GATEWAY PRESS, INC.
Baltimore, MD   2004

No More Goodbyes Ambigram title & cover design
by John Langdon www.johnlangdon.net

Please direct all correspondence and book orders to:
Creative Choices
327 Route 105 W
Jay, VT 05859
email: Linda@soulmission.com

Library of Congress Control Number 2003116452
ISBN 0-9748399-1-4

Published for the authors by
Gateway Press, Inc.
1001 N. Calvert Street
Baltimore, MD 21202-3897

www.Gatewaypress.com

Printed in the United States of America

Dedication

"I dedicate this book to Tai's courageous soul that has chosen to be a part of my life's journey. I have grown because of him and for him. I thank him from the bottom of my heart, which he has worked so hard to open."

Linda M. Brady

"In loving memory of my Great Danes: Casseopia Queen of the Heavens, and Connie Maester...my sweet child... my black-faced Saturn licking dog. Until our souls meet again. And to my Tonkinese cat Kali, who is the embodiment of unconditional loving."

J. C. Landis

"To all my soul contacts and contracts who've helped me along my path: may I be of the same service to them."

Marty Humphreys

Prologue

POM SPEAKS:

I am dying. Each breath escapes with a sigh. Each sigh draws another tear from Linda's blue eyes. You'd think by now, I would have gotten used to saying "goodbye" to my dear Linda. But I'm never really ready to leave her side. Yet this is my time again — again to pass over and head home. If only she understood that I'm at peace it would make things so much easier for both of us. Look at her with the doctor, standing there beside my cage, clutching my red blanket. He must be telling her it's my time to go. It tears me apart to see her in this kind of pain. Spirit pain hurts far worse than mine. My physical pain will end soon but hers…I hate to think how long hers will last.

She opens the door to my cage, gently lifts me into her arms; I always loved the scent of her hair, rustling against my face, tickling my jowls. She strokes my head with her long beautiful fingers. Smiles at me through her tears. Buries her face in the soft black fur on the back of my neck.

My dear Linda, I have not served you well in this lifetime. I must find a way to help you understand I will always come back to you. I will find you no matter where you are. No matter what you look like, or how you change, my soul will always know yours. This is our soul contract through eternity.

The pain returns but I know it will not last. I trust them both to help me with this transition. The doctor moves closer. Forces my mouth open. I'm so weak, so fragile now. I can't resist him. He places something onto my tongue. I swallow. I feel the release of pain from my body. It begins. He pulls my front paw toward him. Instinctively I pull back, and then I remember why we're here. I let him hold it as he presses the needle into my leg. I look up at Linda and lick her good-bye. Then, so gently, so easily, it's over. I am floating. Floating above her. Looking down on my girl…the doctor...my blanket...my withered body.

That's strange. Linda's blue eyes followed me as I rose toward the ceiling. Has she sensed my leaving? Did she see me ascend? I hover around Linda not wanting to leave just yet. I'm sure of it. She does sense my presence, yet my passing brings pain, not peace. Pain I've caused her.

I, too, sense a presence around me that feels so familiar.

Chapter One

"...age of Aquarius...." The Fifth Dimension hit the high note from the portable radio next to Linda's desk. Kelly, her collie dog, panted at her sandaled feet. Wearing a loose fitting cotton blouse and a pair of baggy Bermuda shorts, Linda wished the window air conditioner would either put out more cool air or just die. The rattling drowned out the music, disturbing her concentration. One more exam, then graduation, ending the long road to earning a college degree for someone her stepfather said "would never stick to anything important."

It was May of 1969, and Baltimore's humidity was oppressive as it seeped through every crack in the old farm house, blanketing its inhabitants in a thin layer of sweat. Yawning and stretching Linda renewed her commitment to concentrate on her textbook. The door opened behind her. Kelly perked his ears forward and then rose to investigate.

"Hey, Babe." Joe's voice provided welcomed relief from the heat. Linda turned and smiled at her husband. Big boned, big bodied, Joe's bulk always provided Linda with comfort when life became too much for her.

His arms were filled with black and white fur wrapped in a faded pink blanket. "Brought you something...a pal for Kel and a baby for you." Joe leaned over and gently placed a Pekinese puppy on the wood floor at his feet.

"Joe! What — " the distress in Linda's voice followed her across the room as she rushed to protect the puppy from the larger dog's curiosity. Raising her arm in a protective arc, she turned her back to Kelly. Not to be denied, the collie ducked his head under her arm and stuck his nose on the puppy's head. "Kelly! Oh, Kelly...." Linda's voice softened as she observed Kelly's tail whipping back and forth. It was almost as if they recognized each other, as the pup's welcoming squeaks temporarily relaxed the adults in the room.

"It's not right for a species to live alone," Joe pronounced, as he sank into his favorite chair across the room. "Noah had the right idea.... Besides Kelly is a herder, he will take care of the pup."

Linda looked at her Canadian-born husband and smiled at the biblical reference – very unusual for a man whose Indian heritage more often saw him dabbling in science fiction or metaphysics rather than traditional religion.

Linda had met Joe on a blind date in San Francisco. He was on his way home from his first tour of duty in Viet Nam. He had witnessed some horrific things over there that he would never discuss. But his nighttime flashbacks were a different story: more than once she'd been ejected from their bed and onto the floor, as he shouted at someone, or something, and thrashed around. Come morning, Joe never had any memory of the nightmares, and it certainly wasn't Linda's desire to stir those fears up again.

After a brief career, fulfilling his boyhood dream of becoming a professional hockey player, he had joined the military at 19, needing more structure and discipline in his life. Once in the service he was trained as a medic and saved many lives as part of the 101st Airborne. After their marriage, he had exchanged his Air Force blues for prison khakis when he was hired as a security guard. It was a job he took so Linda could finish her education. He was not much interested in furthering his own. Joe seemed content with his life and his many loves. He was easy going and essentially happy with his woman, his dogs, a good bowling ball, an occasional chess tournament, and his nightly rum and coke.

"Oooof!" Linda exclaimed as the wiggling puppy flew out of her arms for a better look at her new home. Rather than growling at the intruder, Kelly sniffed her thoroughly as she scurried in and out of every corner of the room.

"Puppy, puppy, puppy…come here to Mommy," a smiling Linda leaned over, her hands stretched out toward the wiggling wet nose and large liquid eyes. "Something special about this puppy," she murmured to herself. As Linda squatted down and scooped up the sweet smelling girl, she allowed the puppy's chilly nose to explore the scent on her neck, beneath her chin and behind her ears. Apparently satisfied, the pup's tiny pink tongue signaled her commitment to her new owner as she covered Linda's face with dog kisses. For the moment Kelly had no interest in attacking the newcomer so Linda relaxed and let her heart open to welcome the pup into her life.

Linda grew up in a traditional middle class home in Baltimore County, Maryland. Raised Episcopalian, she regularly attended church with her mother, Betty and her mother's aunt, Marion. Her stepfather rarely went anywhere with the women in the family. Betty's life was devoted to her profession, as head of volunteers at Rosewood, the largest facility in Maryland for developmentally challenged children. Her mother's life was filled with her work, so mothering Linda became her Aunt Marion's responsibility. Perhaps to assuage her guilt for spending more time with other people's children than her own, Betty enlisted Linda as a volunteer at Rosewood from the time Linda was nine years old.

Betty's commitment to her profession was total, in spite of the tragic event that involved a patient and her daughter. On a regular basis one of the adolescent boys from Rosewood came to their house to mow the lawn. During one of these visits one of these boys raped three-year-old Linda. After repairing the damage to her little body, Linda was told to "forgive and forget,"

4

because the boy had no moral sense of what he had done. Linda would often say that it was okay because that boy was not a smart as she was. As punishment he was no longer allowed to mow the lawn at the "little girl's house." As for Linda, this horribly premature "forgiveness" lesson was the first in a string of experiences that would program her to disregard and repress painful feelings. Over time Linda accepted this "get over it" training as a "normal" and rational response to life's hardships, just like Betty's career had been a testament to her ability to maintain professional objectivity and emotional detachment from all those helpless patients.

Even now in her early twenties, Linda was convinced she had put the incident behind her. Yet her failure to reinstate a sense of personal safety and worthiness in her life did not support that conviction.

"What should we call her?" Joe asked from his chair. "She was born in early April, so she's an Aries...."

"Joe, please—like that has anything to do with anything!" Mumbling out loud Linda said, "I think I would like the name Pom, for our little Pekinese pup. Yes, let's call her Pom."

Pom jumped from Linda's arms. Nose down, tail up, she sniffed the aging Oriental rug covering the hardwood floor. Once again the larger dog loomed over her. Linda's heart began to pound as a wave of nausea gripped her stomach.

Arabeth, spiritual guide to animal souls speaks to Linda's unconscious mind:

"Dear one, you're all right. It's going to be OK. I know you're afraid. I can feel your maternal alarm system going off. Your conscious mind has no explanation for how, or why, this furry little stranger could create such an over-protective reaction in you. And yet you can't deny how familiar and connected you feel to this soul. For now, I am asking you to just stay with your instincts and be patient with yourself. This devoted little pup has waited lifetimes for you... to be ready... to need and want her back in your life. This is no first meeting, Linda – this is a reunion. Your heart knows that. It's your mind that can't comprehend the significance of this truth. That's what's making you feel so powerless; Linda – your mind is no longer in full control of your emotions.

"The anxiety over Pom's comfort and safety will continue to arise. That's how she will penetrate your protective emotional shell – the one you built as a toddler to numb yourself from feeling fear and pain. But this time will be different, I promise you. You will be held when you feel most needy and insecure. Facing fear takes great courage, Linda – a quality Pom will teach you to honor in yourself. Her presence will also resurrect old prior-life wounds, which at some level you know the importance of remembering and emotionally re-living. Pom and I have vowed to support and encourage you until you can trust your own guidance system: that of your magnificent soul – the part of God within you.

"You won't consciously remember our conversations. Yet, your soul and I will find gentle ways to make our presence known to you. Through your feelings, intuition and dreams, memories are going to start flooding back into your life. Pay attention, Linda! This is how our souls touch us. Sometimes they bring us symbols, or deja-vu relationships, evoking unconfirmed, yet intense feelings within us. These seemingly unrelated events eventually reach a critical mass that reconstructs a memory we've worked so hard to forget.

"Dear one, this is where we must begin if you are to heal. I will be your guide, your servant, and your protector. I am Arabeth, and I love you."

"Relax, Linda. It's all right...." Joe's reassuring voice stopped her from snatching Pom out of harm's way. Kelly looked down his long nose, and then growled. At first, Pom responded with a growl of her own. Before Kelly could react, Pom charged his throat. Kelly blocked her with his front paw, catching and flipping her onto her back. She wiggled to right herself but not before Kelly placed his paw on her belly keeping her pinned to the floor. Soon angry growls segued into frustration. Linda scooped Pom up and held her out in front of her so they could look at each other eye-to-eye. The sparkle in Pom's eyes proclaimed her fighting spirit and independence.

"So much for the lap dog I picked out for you, Dear." Joe laughed. "I know you've had collies all your life, but it's hard to hold a collie on your lap while you read."

"She's perfect, "Linda replied. "Thank you, Joe."

Linda was aware that her mother's dog, Suki, had had puppies, but never imagined one would find her way to their home. Linda enjoyed watching Pom mature – albeit for the occasional panic attacks Linda couldn't seem to control. Pom was good at cooking up ways to keep Linda's blood pressure pumped. The pup loved to sun herself on the narrow balcony accessible through a second floor window. Kelly had cautioned her to come inside where he could look after her, but his entreaties fell on deaf ears as Pom increased in courage and grew in size. Pom enjoyed leaping from the balcony

7

onto the lawn to chase a neighborhood cat with the hubris to stroll across the yard. On two occasions she was caught in the act when Linda pulled up to witness her transgressions.

Once Linda found the open window, her escape artist was effectively imprisoned in the apartment where she belonged. And, although he could not communicate this to Linda, Kelly was extremely grateful that someone had taken the necessary measures to protect Pom from herself. Being the guardian of this daredevil was more responsibility than Kelly wanted or could handle.

They all spent a lot of time together as Linda studied and prepared for entering the professional work world. Her feelings, and fears, for Pom were so powerful. It just amazed her! Perhaps it was the pup's propensity for risk taking and apparent disregard for her own safety, but her pioneering spirit concerned Linda. She hated leaving Pom alone in the apartment. Even though Kelly was there, Linda's imagination conjured up disasters designed to destroy this precious addition to her life. Anytime Linda was gone she was obsessed with thoughts of fire engulfing the building, robbers breaking in and beating the pup, or worse yet, kidnapping her. In spite of Joe's reassurances, Linda's fears increased. Often her solution was to simply take Pom with her everywhere, which meant she had to park the car where she could see it. On hot days, Linda just adjusted the car's air conditioning before locking Pom inside and taking her spare keys with her.

Chapter Two

The war raged in Viet Nam and the country raged at home, as American women came into their own – no longer satisfied with their exclusive role as "help mates" to their male counterparts. Linda's focus on her future was a distraction from the growing discontent her husband felt at work and at home. He wondered why he should be guarding prisoners here, when his real value was over there saving lives. Perhaps Linda's fears for Pom were a reflection of the paranoia spreading throughout her country in its time of war, or the shift in expectations young women had for themselves as they emerged from the shadows of their men, or denying what was going on in her marriage. Whatever it was, Linda's obsession with Pom's well-being grew daily.

From her place in the universe, Arabeth's deep blue eyes pooled with tears, recognizing Linda's old pattern, with empathy and understanding. She knew all too well Linda's concern was not a reflection of the national distress, rather her automatic reaction to past lifetimes when these two had teamed up before. Their souls' evolution would continue for as many lifetimes as it took, until the universal truths of their soul contract were learned and integrated into their belief systems and habitual behavior patterns.

Arabeth began, "With God's grace, I am honored to be the Spiritual Teacher and Guide to Animal Souls. I am the keeper of the soul contract between person and pet. It is my responsibility to unwaveringly oversee the performance of this binding agreement between Person (Linda) and Pets (Pom et. al.). This contract's Articles #1 – 7, address some of life's most meaningful lessons:

THE SOUL CONTRACT

"Article1: To love all living beings unconditionally and with a full heart.

"Article 2: To honor and experience the full expression of our emotions, so we can:
- Remember that pain creates understanding;
- Learn how to transmute fear into love;
- Share our deepest emotional secrets and not be judged;
- Share our emotions with others to support them in their time of grief and pain.

"Article 3: To remember the mysteries of the other side, so we can:
- Understand that the short life spans of pets help us experience and comprehend the transformational cycle of life and death;
- Understand the process of soul creation;
- Understand the philosophy of reincarnation;
- Learn about soul contracts and the need to honor them.

"Article 4: To welcome our spiritual guides into our life.

"Article 5: To live life without criticism and judgment.

"Article 6: To learn to relate to people with trust and vulnerability.

"Article 7: To learn true perfection through serendipity so we may celebrate and honor life in every precious moment."

Arabeth continued, "...The prehistoric connection humans have developed with their pets is for many, their primary and most loving *relationship. Animals can be trusted to authentically express what they feel, whereas humans develop defenses and repress some of their deepest feelings. Pets, in contrast, work hard to establish open, dependable, and unconditionally loving relationship bonds. For millennia, they have served humans as role-models for building healthy, mutually-nurturing heart connections.*

"There is much to learn, dear child, and you have an able teacher to assist you in your spiritual growth."

After mailing numerous job applications and attending follow up interviews, Linda accepted the position of Director of Rehabilitation Therapy at a new state center for mentally challenged children. She would have her own department to build and a new staff to train. She would supervise art, occupational, recreational and musical therapists, and have an opportunity to integrate these services into the lives of her new charges. As a recent college graduate, Linda was thrilled, yet surprised with the job offer since it carried far more responsibility and authority than she expected. That was true of every job she had ever held – being entrusted with responsibility beyond her qualifications, once again she would quickly grow into this position and receive excellent reviews and assessments.

Linda took Pom to her mother's house where she spent each day with her litter mates and parents until Linda could pick her up.

If Joe objected to his wife's obsession, he kept it to himself, as he was preoccupied with more personal problems. He feared returning to the wild days of his youth if he continued in his current job. He knew it was time to re-enlist and do his duty. He hated to leave Linda and the dogs, but this job was killing his spirit. He had left the Air Force so Linda could finish her degree and begin a career. He desperately missed the meaningfulness, and adrenaline rush, of saving lives. Now that Linda's career was moving forward it was his turn to return to his passion of being a medic. But how to tell Linda....

During one of those visits at Betty's house, Pom went through her first heat and became pregnant. Linda decided to let her have the puppies and find good homes for them once they were weaned.

Only a few days after birthing the pups Pom showed signs of being a conflicted mother. She missed joining Linda on her errands. Simply the sound of Linda's car keys created moments of anxiety and indecision for Pom. She'd pop out of the puppy box and follow Linda to the door. Looking up at her with those large eyes, Pom would dutifully shift her attention back to her pups and succumb to the demands of motherhood.

Watching Pom mother her puppies, Linda began to examine how similar they were. If she and Joe had children, she too would do her duty by them, but feel claustrophobic and resent the loss of freedom. In her late twenties, they had postponed that decision until she finished her education and Joe found a line of work he enjoyed. She had accomplished her goal, but knew in her heart Joe was still far from his. Observing Pom's

14

conflict reinforced Linda's decision not to have children yet, if ever.

"Linda, my dear child, now is the time to start reconnecting you with your feelings. Little Pom is beginning to crack you open – to show you what you haven't been able to show yourself, or learn to feel for other humans – how to love another, by putting aside all criticism and judgment.

"Do you believe it is merely a coincidence that Pom has become a conflicted mother, constantly having to choose between her pups and being with you? This is true serendipity. She's not only helping you discern what you 'think' about motherhood, but how you 'feel' about ever becoming a mother.

"Just like your mother, you've created a career of caring for others, yet find it difficult to determine what you emotionally need to feel nurtured yourself. I watch you fill your life with constant activity… staying in perpetual motion to keep distracted and disconnected from your emotions. So I ask you, dear one, how can you trust yourself to know what will make you happy if you continue to resist your own feelings and hide from your fears?

"You're not the only human who holds this belief. It's a familiar self-deception you choose to perpetuate…wanting to believe you can minimize or even avoid, the grief and sorrow accompanying loss and separation, if you control HOW MUCH you allow yourself to love. Linda, this illusion has prevented you from fully opening your heart and experiencing unconditional love. More important is the awareness that this defensive posture has never really kept you from being hurt. Do you realize that?"

New, previously unconsidered ideas began to preoccupy Linda's mind crowding out whatever quiet she was able to salvage from her frenetic days. She began asking herself questions about her working habits, her future with Joe, her paranoia with Pom's well being, her feelings about ever being a mother....Where were they coming from? Why wouldn't they leave her alone?

Days later, Joe came home with a handful of paperwork. Linda's pupils dilated with apprehension, knowing instinctively what it meant: he was returning to the Air Force.

"When?"

"As soon as the ink dries." Joe looked up smiling.

"Where will you go?"

Joe paused, filling out the form. "Viet Nam again, I hope."

Linda squeezed her eyes closed and shook her head. "You'll forgive me if I hope not."

"Sure, Honey. Sure. They'll send me someplace else first–stateside, then...."

"Will I have to go with you?" Linda's mouth fell open, hearing the insensitivity of her words echo in her head. "Joe, I didn't mean that—I meant, can we all go with you?"

Joe turned away to conceal the rejection he felt. "You were right the first time. You don't have to go anywhere you don't want to go...."

She knew immediately from his body language, she couldn't have hurt him any more if she had brutally beaten him. The day arrived for Joe to leave for Scott Air Force Base in Bellevue, Illinois. He didn't want her to drive him to the airport. He preferred to say their good-byes in the apartment, where they had shared

16

so much happiness. Linda broke the embrace and leaned away from him. Looking into his eyes, she said, "It won't be too long before we see each other again." One last hug, one last kiss, and he pulled open the door to leave.

Tugging his duffel bag through the door, he leaned back inside. "You are coming to Illinois, aren't you?"

For the next six months, Linda worked at The Center. With Joe gone, her loneliness was counterbalanced by the heavy workload she relished and the devoted companionship she had found with Pom and Kelly. During this separation Linda learned, much to her surprise, she was very content living a single's life. She was grateful to Joe for temporarily giving up his career for hers, but now felt the weight of her obligation to join him in Illinois. For the first time in her life she was beginning to realize her professional potential, and how vital a graduate degree would be to her future. It was difficult leaving her wonderful position, but getting more education would be a valuable use of her time.

Chapter Three

The road sped by the car windows as Linda and Pom rode the ribbon west to Illinois. She was concerned with Kelly making the trip by car, so she asked Betty to put him on the plane after she arrived at her destination. Driving had always been one of Linda's favorite pastimes, and this trip gave her the opportunity to escape the self-inflicted pace of her work schedule. Listening to loud music and enjoying the scenery, she and Pom were loving their independence. Alone with her thoughts Linda smiled, thinking that maybe people not only get to look like their pets, but act like them as well...or was this an example of what Jung called "projection"?

Base housing was not their first choice, but it was all they could afford. After the furniture shipment arrived, they picked Kelly up at the airport very groggy from the flight.

Linda wasted no time enrolling in Southern Illinois University for her Masters degree in Educational Administration. Classes and studies took up every spare moment. Joe was gone most of the time on training missions with the Air Force, during which Linda shared long walks around the base with Kelly and Pom. In early April 1971, after one of their invigorating walks, the trio entered their apartment to find Joe there with a new four poster dog bed and a bright red blanket. "Happy Birthday, Baby," Joe smiled broadly presenting Pom with her second birthday present. "Red for a warrior, my brave girl." Wagging her tail enthusiastically, Pom jumped on the oaken four-poster dog bed and sniffed the blanket. Grabbing it in her teeth, she shook it, circled twice, and then settled in.

"Success!" Joe mused over dinner. "I had several color choices for a blanket, but this one seemed the best. And I thought dogs were color blind...."

"How would we know...really?" Linda answered. "It does seem to please her, though."

Pom demonstrated an unusual attachment to the blanket, dragging it behind her everywhere she went. At the time, Linda had no idea how well the color suited her Arian dog.

As a child, Linda had been painfully shy. Her shyness continued into adulthood complicated by a slight stutter whenever she became nervous. Her native intelligence and old-world work ethic produced excellent grades in high school and college. It was enough without having to speak out and "show herself," her Aunt Marion would say. That had been true until now. Her newest professor's reputation was that he believed women did not belong in male-dominated administrative professions, or in his classroom, for that matter. He challenged her every time she came through the door. Eventually she would have to venture out of her shell, stand up for what she believed, and show him, and herself, exactly what she was made of. On one hand, she lived in fear of that day arriving…on the other hand she was beginning to welcome such challenges. There was no doubt about it…her self-confidence was growing.

All aspects of the Viet Nam War filled both television and newspaper content. Every evening Linda wondered what she could do to help. She was a skillful listener, so she decided to spend time with the young soldiers in transition from Viet Nam, coming back to stateside. Not knowing how they would be received, there was often little conversation, but she would sit with them waiting for them to talk. At least they would know someone cared enough to be there if they needed to share anything about their experiences.

Linda's life fell into a comfortable routine. On the rare occasion Joe was home, they would settle in along with the rest of the country, and watch the carnage on the evening news. Linda looked on in disbelief as civilians protested the war at home. She believed in her country and its mission over there. Almost every man on base had either been there or was scheduled to go soon. While living in Baltimore she attempted to get Joe to talk about his experiences, but that catatonic stare was the only answer she ever got.

Why would Joe be so eager to go back and relive the very scenes that disturbed his sleep on a nightly basis? One night she made the mistake of waking him while he was violently thrashing around. He awoke with a start, and lunged at her, his hands grasping for her throat. Pom's frantic bark penetrated his dream state as his rage dissolved into tears of shame for threatening her.

Later that month Joe brought a young private home for dinner. After much beer and sympathetic urging from Linda, he told them of a patrol he had been on, during which he'd killed a four-year-old Vietnamese girl. She approached his patrol carrying a basket, in which he suspected she had a bomb. His survival instincts, and training, told him to "shoot first and ask questions later." After searching through the basket's contents he found only three old eggs. Linda couldn't take her eyes off of him as he conveyed his story, completely and totally devoid of emotion. Linda flushed with regret for ever having probed him in the first place. He had no observable emotion-based reaction to the incident whatsoever – absolutely none. His complete detachment seemed inhuman, yet this is how most of us survive such unimaginable horror and guilt – we simply disconnect ourselves from the felt experience. She wondered how many felt remorse for what they'd done, or forgiveness for what had been done to them. She also grieved for her countrymen, most of whom didn't want to know any of these soldiers' stories. Ignorance, in THIS case, was bliss.

That night after going to bed, Linda asked Joe when he'd get his orders and where he would go. "Any day now – and probably Nam." With that, he rolled over onto his stomach and was asleep before she could ask her follow up questions.

A week later, her arms full of textbooks and groceries, Linda entered their apartment. Staggering to the couch, she dumped the books, and then continued to the kitchen with the groceries. Kelly greeted her with a smile and a tail wag, while Pom scampered around her ankles asking to be picked up and petted. "Just a minute…Mommy's arms are full." She unpacked the Commissary bags, putting the orange juice and milk into their small refrigerator, then bent over and stroked Kelly's head before gathering Pom into her arms.

Suddenly, Kelly turned and streaked to the front door. The living room door flew open and Joe entered. "Hey!"

Startled, Linda looked up at the door, and then glanced at the round clock on the wall. "You're early?"

"Yeah." Joe leaned over and tickled Kelly behind his ears. "I got my orders today."

Chilly fingers massaged Linda's spine as she clutched Pom more tightly in her arms. "Orders...?" Flashes of wounded and dying men on The Huntley-Brinkley Report filled her mind.

"Uh, huh. The Philippines." Joe approached his wife, arms

23

opened out, anticipating a hug. Still gripping Pom tightly to her chest, Linda turned away. Undaunted by her response, Joe slipped his arms around both of them from behind. "The good news is that it is accompanied. Our family can travel intact— they allow dogs in the Philippines. It could have been worse; it could have been Hawaii. There's still a six-month quarantine for animals there."

Good news for him, but Linda was not convinced. "But I've got three more months to finish my Masters."

"It will take that long for the unit to move and for me to locate appropriate housing for us—you'll have plenty of time to finish before joining me."

His soft voice murmured reassurances. Still, Linda wasn't so sure.

A new weather pattern had moved into the area with rolling thunderstorms in the late afternoon. Between classes, the clouds opened, pouring a tank load of water onto the campus. Sheets of rain mixed with rocks of hail as Linda raced across the lawn. She didn't mind the wetness, but the pellets of ice hurt. Following a parade of other students and professors, she dashed beneath an overhang to wait the hailstorm out. To release tension, everyone seemed to have a comment.

"Wow, did you feel that?"

"Umbrellas do no good in this stuff…."

"Looks like a scene from Viet Nam...."

"Yeah, without the napalm."

No one laughed at the student's weak attempt at a joke. After numerous violent incidents on campuses across the country, people were sensitive to political commentary from any source. Because of her association to the military, Linda maintained a discreet silence whenever possible.

"Looks more like monsoon season in the Philippines...." from behind a baritone voice broke the silence.

Linda turned to find its source and discovered a pleasant-looking middle-aged man...probably a professor. The hail continued its drumbeat on the metal roof above, as Linda summoned the courage to ask him about her impending destination.

"Excuse me...but have you been to the Philippines?" she asked.

"You mean lately?"

"Yes, lately...my husband has orders to go there...."

"Lucky you...."

Linda couldn't tell if she heard sarcasm in his voice, so she pressed on. "I guess it's better than Viet Nam—for him, I mean."

"Do you have children?" he asked.

"Uh, no, not yet. We have two dogs...."

A frown shadowed the man's face. "That's probably worse...."

25

"What?" Linda recognized a familiar cold shiver, but attributed it to the cold rain falling around her. "Why?"

The man looked over her shoulder before answering. "We had a friend there who brought his German Shepherd with him—a local stole him, then sold him to the market as food."

Linda caught the scream before it escaped her throat. "Oh, my God!"

"Yes, he saw him the following weekend hanging in the marketplace."

Hot tears sprang to her eyes in stark contrast to the chill crawling down her spine. "Th, Th, Thank you. I mean for the information...." she said. Her decision made, she bolted across the quad to her classroom. Her intuition had proved to be accurate. She was ambivalent about accompanying Joe to the Philippines, but until that coincidental meeting wasn't sure why—now, she knew. She would not take Kelly or Pom to that place! If the truth had been known, a sizable weight had been lifted from her heart. It was time to tell Joe....

That evening, Linda defended her decision not to go. Joe listened, challenged some of her points, but finally accepted the verdict. There was no changing her mind. Their remaining days together were tension-filled and spent mostly in silence. Whether it was fear, grief or the anxiety accompanying any major life change, both of them clearly felt it. Joe had left on flights so many times, but this time was different, very different. Kelly sensed the strain between them feeling a need to pay more attention to Joe than usual.

The day of his departure Linda drove Joe to the airfield at 3:00 AM. After a long embrace and whispered endearments, Joe leaned over, kissed each of the dogs, and backed out of the passenger seat pulling his duffel bag out after him.

"Take care of yourself, Linda...."

"Take care of yourself, Joe...."

She watched him walk toward the large transport plane. Unlike the rest of the men, he didn't turn around to wave one last time. He was too proud for her to see his tears.

Linda realized it was easier than she had anticipated.... she didn't miss Joe as much as she thought she would. Perhaps it was Linda's imagination, but Kelly seemed depressed and aloof those first few weeks. He seemed to have lost interest in both Linda and Pom. Kelly's behavior only contributed to the mountain of guilt Linda already felt for not accompanying her husband overseas. Did she care more for her dogs than the man she loved and married? As the time passed she began to wonder if, indeed, she did.

Chapter Four

Packing the apartment up for her return to Baltimore involved boxes, oceans of paper, and mounds of tape. The morning of her last class, Linda drank a gallon of coffee and smoked two packs of cigarettes, as she incessantly paced the floor. She had one more class and was then free to leave. Naturally, it was the class she hated, feared, and was intimidated by the most. Since she had been the only female in his class, he took out most of his anti-feminist prejudices on her. Linda had been able to hide behind her shyness until today. In the last class he had challenged her to role-play the "autocratic educator" as part of her final exam. Her performance counted for a full third of her grade.

Shaking in her sandals, she entered the classroom. He greeted her with a smirk and a sweeping gesture to move to the front of the classroom. The previously friendly faces of her classmates passed before her in a blur as she marched to the isolated podium. After a few throat-clearings and several deep breaths, she pulled her package of Marlboro Reds from her shoulder bag, shook out a cigarette, popped it between her lips and lit up. Between drags her voice was strong and sure as she gained power and momentum. Initially too frozen by fear to even notice the professor's reaction she proceeded with her presentation until the last note card had been spoken. Finally she faced the professor. Arching her eyebrow as if to say, "Well?" she held her breath.

The seconds expanded until he looked up from his notes. "One word, Linda. Only one word: Bravo!" he smiled at her. "But, next time...lose the cigarette. Those things can kill you...."

Linda was so intoxicated with delight she didn't remember what route she took back to the apartment. She had found her voice and couldn't wait to get home to share her joy with her canine family. From this day forward, Linda would sing instead of stutter her message to the world.

Moving day. June 15, 1973.

Linda muttered as she organized their household goods into two piles: one for donation and one to move. Pom and Kelly played hide and seek among the sealed boxes. Grabbing a roll of duck tape, Pom scooted beneath the coffee table. Kelly charged after her only to run into the table, shoving it into the couch. Pom yelped more in surprise than in pain. Linda rushed to her side, swept her up off the floor and examined her for broken bones, of which there were none. She buried her face in Pom's neck. All was well in the world when she and Pom were exchanging affection.

Apparently sensing a shift in his master's feelings, Kelly moved to her side pushing his head into her leg. She reached down to include him in their circle of love. Crying softly, she sank into the sofa beside the dogs. Her tears were interrupted by a solid knock on the front door. The movers had arrived. They fanned into the room, and started carrying boxes out the door.

"Do these go?" the mover pointed to the biggest pile in the corner.

"No, I'm giving that stuff away."

"All of this? What happened? Did you win bingo at St. Cecilias?"

Laughing, she replied. "Nope, I travel light".

"I'll say," the mover gave her an appreciative glance.

Linda blushed when she realized he was flirting with her. She had been overweight since she entered adolescence. She weighed 220 pounds when she met and married Joe. She'd gained another 40 pounds after the wedding. Since the move to Illinois, and Joe's departure to the Philippines, she'd shed most of the fat from her 5'5" inch frame, and had become aware of other men's admiring glances. That, too, was a first for Linda. Joe's voice echoed in her ear, "If you lose anymore weight, I'm going to lose you...."

The mover bent over to pack Pom's bed and blanket. She

sprang from Linda's arms and grabbed a corner of the blanket on its way up and into the last open box. Growling, Pom yanked the blanket out of the mover's hands, retrieving it back to the safety of Linda's feet.

Loading everything but two suitcases, and Pom's blanket, the apartment looked as empty as Linda felt. She surveyed the rooms one last time before hustling her family out of the apartment and onto the road headed home to Baltimore. With the sunset behind her, Linda crossed the state line into Ohio. Armed with her new Masters degree and several favorable responses to her mailed job survey, she straightened her shoulders and arched her back against the car seat. As if reading her mind, Kelly glanced over at Linda. At last, Linda sensed Kelly's understanding and forgiveness, for her decision to stay behind rather than join Joe in the Philippines.

After the flat countryside of Ohio, the mountains of West Virginia rose up along the horizon in beauty as Linda continued to push east. There was no hurry. They could take their time. Her furniture wouldn't even be shipped until she located a place to send it to.

Thinking back to her life as a military wife, she would miss the sense of being associated with something bigger than she was but she wouldn't miss the people on the base. Joe and Linda had been anomalies among their military contemporaries.

As in all areas of her life, Linda led with questions, and continued to question, until she received satisfactory answers—which typically provoked more questions. In order to be comfortable in the military arena, questions were not invited and when asked, not answered. It didn't surprise Linda when "Don't Ask, Don't Tell" became a policy covering almost every area of controversy in the military.

Shortly after arriving in Baltimore, Pom's personality transformed from assertive to apathetic. From awake and aware, to aloof and sluggish. At first, Linda attributed it to the stress of another move, then to Joe's absence, and then finally realized the changes were due to Pom's "heat" cycle. As if that wasn't troubling enough Kelly began to annoy Linda by constantly whining up at her, then looking over at Pom, usually asleep on her red blanket. Inviting a snappy comeback, Linda approached the bed where she slept but Pom didn't even lift her head at the sound of Linda's voice. Glancing at Kelly sitting next to the pup, Linda realized with a start what her companion had been trying to tell her. Pom was sick, very sick and Linda was solely responsible for taking care of her.

From somnolence to shivers, Pom awoke and began to shake all over on the trip to the vet's office. Linda could not watch as the vet drew blood from her tiny foreleg.

"This is just a precaution. From the symptoms you describe, it sounds like a kidney infection to me," the vet explained. "I highly recommend you have her spayed as soon as this infection clears up...make an appointment on your way out, OK?"

Linda felt sick at even the mention of an operation. She nodded her agreement, thanked the vet, and stopped at the reception desk to pay her bill.

"Do you want to make an appointment for the operation now?" asked the receptionist.

"No, no thank you...I'll call next week," Linda lied as she raced out the door to escape the decision.

Back in the car, Linda shook uncontrollably. Relief, then fear, seized her central nervous system. The thought of putting Pom to sleep for an operation was too frightening to consider. Linda vowed to keep a close watch over Pom, whenever she came into heat, to prevent another potentially fatal pregnancy.

It didn't take Linda long to find and accept the position of an evening ER Clerk at Baltimore County Hospital. She needed a Ph.D. to feel confident in this line of work. This job would give her an opportunity to go to school during the day when she enrolled in the fall. Months went by as Linda awaited Joe's return from the Philippines. Letters were exchanged and occasionally Joe made a tape for them to listen to detailing his experiences overseas. He strongly criticized the military's running of this absurd war. He spoke of his love for them, how much he missed them and looked forward to coming home. The first time Linda played a tape for Pom and Kelly, she wished she had photographed their expressions as they listened to the sound of Joe's voice.

Long periods of time passed when Linda didn't receive any word from Joe. Those dry spells lasted for weeks. As the communications dwindled so did Linda's connection and attachment to her husband. She became involved with a respiratory therapist in an intense affair. This was the first time in her life she really felt attractive, and she wasn't about to waste a single day of this newly found popularity. Just like her mom, she had always been so responsible and dedicated to making something of herself. This was her chance to take life less seriously and finally have some fun! "Make love, not war," were the catchwords of the day, and Linda made that her mantra.

One morning on her way to work at County, she was driving her favorite car, a 1970 white Camaro with a black top and sun roof. Singing at the top of her lungs to her favorite rock and roll radio station, she did not see the on-coming car until it hit her head-on. The near-death collision injured her head and back, creating memory loss, vision problems, and a lot of neck and back pain. Her recovery took months, during which she lost her job and had no choice but to return to her mother's house to live.

Financially unprepared to enroll for more graduate work, Linda joined her mother at Rosewood Center. Caring for the mentally handicapped was the highest calling for those courageous enough to do the work – a philosophy Linda shared with her mother. The institution accommodated 3000 residents and hid some of the worst housing conditions imaginable. Patients were warehoused because of the severity of their disabilities. As a diagnostic specialist, Linda's duties included: diagnosing the children's educational needs; placing them in appropriate classroom settings to learn basic, daily living skills; and providing vocational experience, if appropriate. Her mother was referred to as Saint Betty, because of the work she had done there for decades. Now that Linda had her Master's Degree in Education, it seemed logical to return to Rosewood and apply her skills.

Her days revolved around the endless amount of work, in the under-funded, under-staffed institution. Her nights were spent carrying on downtown. Her communications with Joe decreased to almost nothing, then finally ceased all together.

During one of her clubbing dates, Linda met Peter, a trumpet player in a band she and her groupie friends followed. He was also a practicing predictive astrologer. At first, she pretended to listen and accept what he had to say because of her tremendous attraction to him. But eventually their relationship developed into a six-month running argument, as Linda continued to challenge the validity of astrology and its application in people's lives. Peter became so frustrated with her cynicism he refused to discuss the subject any longer, until or unless she knew half as much as he did about this ancient wisdom. Ironically, once Linda became a serious student, Peter disappeared from her life. Raised in a traditional, protestant family, astrology was at best superstition…at worst, the work of the devil. None of that mattered to Linda, not if it answered her questions.

"Predictive Astrology is popular among the humans who do not believe they are personally responsible for creating their own lives. They see themselves as having no control over their present or future. In other words, all is pre-ordained and life is what happens TO them.

"In contrast Karmic Astrology asserts the importance of utilizing one's free will, guided by the soul's ultimate wisdom, rather than merely being informed in advance of their 'inevitable fate'. This longer view includes the concepts of reincarnation and soul missions, and the on-going evolution of the soul over numerous lifetimes. Being the persecutor in one lifetime, and victim in the next, generates a depth of informed understanding and heart-felt compassion that only first hand experience can create. Now we have both reaped and sown the same karmic lesson from a dualistic perspective. Only then does one truly KNOW, not merely conceptualize, the felt experience of 'walking in another's shoes'.

"Dear Linda, your path is pure perfection....For at least 3,000 years our ancestors have valued and utilized the symbolic language of Karmic Astrology to decode and uncover the hidden web work of their souls' spiritual agenda – that which their conscious personality did not always recognize."

With her personal life in shambles, she poured herself into her work. Those fifteen-hour days may have proved her value to the world but not to herself. Insecurity, anxiety and fear still filled her life, especially when she'd leave Pom alone in the evenings.

The day started normally. Marion woke her at 7 AM so Linda would have time for coffee with her mother. As accommodating as her mother and aunt had been, Linda knew this living arrangement was not helping her new found social life. It was time to find her own place. Linda fixed the dogs their breakfast before saying "goodbye" for the day. Kelly preferred the out-of-doors, while Pom circled and dropped into her basket to snuggle down with her prized red blanket. "Be good, kids. Mommy will be back soon, and then we'll go house hunting together...." As was her habit, she gave each of them a scratch and kiss before sailing out the door.

Always the first teacher at the school, she unlocked the side door to the brick pillared Georgian building, and trotted down the steps into her small basement office. There was a great window overlooking the forest behind this administration building. The office was small, and filled with plants her friends guaranteed her she could not kill. Photographs of Pom and Kelly encircled her wooden desktop. Checking her inbox, she grabbed the new intake file marked "Mary" from the top and went to look for Patrick, her Vice Principal. Sticking her head inside his office she gave him the high sign. He quickly joined her in the walk to the hospital.

As usual, the sour smell of the hospital assaulted her nostrils as soon as Patrick opened the door for her to walk through. It wasn't just her recent, personal hospitalization that made her uncomfortable; this unique smell had always made her uneasy. As the tips of her heels tapped a rapid rhythm on the institutional tile floor, Linda marveled at how drab the surroundings were in spite of futile attempts to enhance the atmosphere with cheap colorful prints. These walls were intended to keep the "damaged people" in, as to not inflict their pain on the "normal people" outside the perimeter. Shaking her head to rid herself of these destructive depressing thoughts, Linda pushed open the heavy door into Mary's room, as Patrick followed right behind. Centered in the cold room, strapped into her wheel chair, little Mary's tortured body slumped forward, her head almost on her knees.

"Oh my God...." Linda exclaimed as she stopped short. Patrick ran right into her heels. As Mary raised her eyes, Linda saw a translucent aura surrounding her head. Straight, ultra-fine light brown hair framed her pale little, expressionless face. Large, light blue eyes stared into space. Was there really a person inside that body?

Linda's eyes narrowed, and then glanced at the window hoping to detect the source of light illuminating this child's head. The windowpanes were painted with a semi-opaque yellowish paint, allowing ambient, but not specific light into the room. Opening Mary's file, Linda noticed her IQ was barely 10. Her cerebral palsy caused her limbs to twitch with irregular spasms. Linda took a deep breath then forced herself to approach the child.

The room was cold. Linda shivered stopping eight feet from her wheelchair. Tears began to burn her eyes as her cool-calm-and-collected objectivity melted away. Bile rose in the back of her throat. Linda swallowed hard to keep her breakfast where it belonged. What could this child have done to deserve this? Mary's body continued to glow with a blinding light. Linda had read about this type of paranormal experience, sometimes described as a halo, in comparative religion books. These clinical textbooks intentionally eliminated any emotive references to this phenomenon – all word choices helped the student maintain a safe, conceptual and personally removed response. But this light was not of this world and it petrified Linda.

Uncontrollably, out of her fear erupted rage. From deep inside her heart Linda shook her fist at the God who could allow such a thing to occur in the world. If He was so intelligent, why would ignorance and hatred persist? If He was so perfect, why did He allow Mary to be born, and to exist in such a condition without hope for a better future?

Linda's fragile mask of professionalism cracked and slipped away. Apparently forgetting Patrick was in the room, she turned and plowed right into him.

"Oh, Patrick, I'm sorry...I've got to go home...I'm, uh, I'm sick...."she sobbed back at him as she fled the room, the building, and her life. Driving fast, she slammed the car to a stop at an angle in front of her mother's house. Grabbing her purse, she ran from the car to the front door. Keys rattling in her shaking hands, Linda found the keyhole and shoved the key home. Perhaps her noisy arrival woke the dogs from their morning nap. Or perhaps they sensed her fear the way dogs do, but they met her inside the doorway without the happy tail wagging of normal greetings. Rather they sat and stared at her until her body was entirely inside the safety of her space.

Dropping her bag, Linda opened her arms to gather her companions to her. Licking her face, neck and ears, the dogs welcomed her home. At their touch, her tears flowed freely until she had no more to cry. Their joyful expressions of affection blatantly contrasted to the total absence of any emotion in Mary's life – Linda's heart simply over-flowed with immense gratitude. Sitting cross-legged on the floor in the entryway, she pulled Pom into her lap. Kelly curled up beside them. All the questions withheld until now flowed from her heart into the open.

Linda found her voice. "Where is the perfect God who could eliminate Mary's suffering, her pain, and the pain her parents must feel every time they look at their daughter's crippled body? And, what is so perfect about a world inhabited by children like Mary?" After the anger subsided, Linda sat, her arms still around her precious friends, wondering why this experience was so powerful and so different. She had been around these children for almost thirty years, now this!

"Dear one, you're safe now." This familiar voice was barely audible. She spoke in a modulated, compassionate tone. "You made it home. Pom and Kelly are close by your side. I want you to try and relax. Take a few deep, slow, gentle breaths. Tenderly, allow your breath to dissolve your anxiety, apprehensions, and that hard protective shell.

"Simply as an observer, I want you to notice where in your body the anger and fear has lodged itself. Your mouth is dry. Your tear ducts are flooding making it difficult to see clearly. Your skin is moist and clammy. You're conscious of how full your lungs need to be before your chest pains diminish in intensity.

"What's happening? Why has this shaken you so? Let yourself sink into your feelings.... What are you resisting Linda? What is it you're afraid to feel? You can touch this place in you in this moment, with us holding you. It would have only been natural for you to feel grief and sadness for Mary, but why rage? Your anger is a distraction, push through it. Something is buried within YOU that is bringing that emotion into the light.

"For lifetimes you've used discipline and self-control to protect yourself from these feelings but it's not working anymore. Even your body is trying to get your attention by showing you all these physical reactions. There's no more escape. Something is changing.

"A thought arises. You're afraid to share this secret with anyone. How will it make you look? You're a professional! Respected and trusted as a levelheaded educator! You've worked hard to maintain that grounded, practical, logical image. How will you explain the lunacy you've experienced? No one will understand if YOU can't make sense of it. Can you find the words? Do you even have the language to articulate such an out-of-body experience? Worse yet, this vision threatens to topple the view YOU hold of your entire world! Fearing your foundational beliefs are about to shatter, you won't even try to rationalize this for YOURSELF! Where will you look for safety?

Structure? Answers? What will keep you from falling into the abyss? Where will you find faith now, Linda? In what, or with whom, can you place your trust now?

"These are just thoughts... projections into the future... another distraction from your feelings! No matter. What's important is the surfacing of these questions for which you have no traditional, pat, answers.

"You've done well, my courageous child. I am proud of you for wading into this feeling-pool. Now rest. Rest, dear Linda. The answers are coming."

Her listless body slumped over. Her pets snuggled closer. She couldn't remember ever being as tired as she was at that moment. All those years of pushing herself fused right here. As Pom licked her face, she told her of the aura surrounding Mary's head. "Is this child a saint, an angel? Have I been given an incredible gift to perceive the divinity of this child? Or have I been cursed because I hold so many judgments about this world filled with such unreasonable pain?"

Arabeth continued to observe this scene. She urged Pom to comfort Linda.

"Seeing this aura is a gift from God, Linda. Now it's up to you to understand it's not only Mary who has a special message and mission—but each living thing on earth. She is here to remind others to appreciate, celebrate and honor life in every precious moment.

"Mary is a high-level soul who requested an incarnation to serve all those who made contact with her. What you've seen, my dear child, is Mary's soul energy. It appears as light so humans will recognize it

for what it is – pure, divine energy of the highest order, the same energy of which ALL our souls are made."

Feeling comforted without really understanding why, Linda reviewed her options. No longer certain of the tenets she held, Linda was determined to understand this event. It was too profound not to have meaning, but how to access the purpose, the message, the action now expected of her? How could she continue her work at Rosewood under such a profound burden of anger and guilt? Perhaps she couldn't.

The first step was to find a place of her own to live, where she could create the quiet and solitude needed to reflect on this life-altering experience. Grabbing the newspaper she flipped to the "Apartment for Rent" section and picked up the phone. Smiling at her pets, she assured them everything would be all right. She wondered to whom she was talking.

After they had found a suitable apartment and moved, Linda's routine resumed. Unconsciously she added longer work hours to her day to keep her mind preoccupied and her demons at bay. Feeling guilty for leaving her dogs alone so much she arranged for her Aunt Marion to "baby" sit the dogs while she worked. This arrangement added more time to Linda's commute but who cared if her animals were happy and her own fears diminished.

A few weeks later, Linda bent over to pick Pom up when she noticed her swollen abdomen. A cold sheet of fear washed over her. Immediately she called the vet to insist upon

44

the next appointment.

They rushed to the animal doctor's office and waited to be seen. Pom wiggled under the vet's large hands as he examined her. "When was her last heat?" he asked looking up at Linda.

Her mind went blank. "I can't remember...oh, no. Please don't tell me she's pregnant."

"I hope she is, otherwise this size swelling could indicate something far more serious. Let's do an ultrasound and we'll find out."

Pom's pregnancy was not good news. Considering her kidney difficulties, this pregnancy and birthing could kill her. Linda couldn't hold back the obvious question: "Will she survive it?"

The vet smiled reassuringly and nodded. "Sure she will— but this must be the last one, OK?"

Linda couldn't stop chastising herself. If only she'd had her beloved dog fixed after the last pregnancy. She glanced over at Pom, curled up in deep sleep on the passenger seat of the Camaro. Feeling Linda's concern, Pom opened her eyes and appeared to smile hoping to alleviate Linda's guilt.

That night Linda called Joe in the Philippines to warn him of Pom's condition. She reassured him she would cut back on her hours to spend more time with their pup. Her intentions were good but faded in a few days. The need to escape her guilt dominated her commitment to Joe. Keeping busy was her pattern and favorite escape – resuming her mindless commitment to work was automatic.

Chapter Five

Linda watched Pom's belly expand to accommodate the puppies. With each noticeable change a vague specter of the past continued to darken Linda's days. Worry is only anger projected into the future, she told herself, but that wasn't the only thing that was emptying her life of joy. Her marriage to Joe was as good as over and she couldn't shake the sense of discomfort and apprehension that infiltrated her world since the auric phenomenon. If she didn't talk to someone about the halo she was going to go nuts! She hoped her associate Patrick could help her regain some peace.

Patrick was always a good sounding board for Linda's more heretical thoughts, as well as her job performance and professional future. He was initially a seminary student but chose marriage and family over his commitment to the priesthood. As she formulated her thoughts, Patrick came into the cafeteria suggesting that they take time for some coffee. Having second thoughts about destroying her self-image with him she almost declined until another voice took over, "Yes, I'd love a cup."

They got in line together, grabbed a mug, poured the coffee and sat down at a small private table in the corner. Linda wanted to make sure no one could hear the details of their conversation.

There they sat, in silence, until Patrick began. "Linda, you haven't been yourself lately," looking directly into her bloodshot blue eyes. "You're working more and clearly enjoying it less."

She laughed and let her guard down a little. "Oh, you noticed," she said, rehearsing her thoughts as she watched the creamer dissolve from powder to swirling liquid in the cup.

"Anything I can do?" Patrick's greatest gift was patience. Unlike most people, he'd wait for a response to his query rather than jump in and answer his question for you.

Linda sighed, then shared her experience of the encounter with Mary. "Patrick am I losing my mind, or did I really see an angel?"

He looked up and then around them. "All of Rosewood's children are angels – we are all angels."

"Don't patronize me! I'm serious about this!" Linda felt the tears rising but forced them back into their ducts through sheer will power. "You were right behind me, Patrick! Did you see or sense anything?"

He raised his eyebrows and shook his head. "All right, maybe not all of us are angels...did you say the light filled the room?"

"No, but now that I think about it, it surrounded her— providing an aura of at least 18 inches—it was almost like a protective shield.... My God! I am not the enemy, am I?"

"That depends," he grinned, trying to relax his co-worker and friend — "on what your academic assessment of her was."

Linda's posture straightened as she pursed her lips. "I left before I had an opportunity to create one...." Clearly Linda was in no mood for teasing.

"And why do you suppose you, but not I, were meant to see the aura?"

"If I knew the answer to that we wouldn't be here talking now would we?" Linda quipped back. Then, finding safety in his willingness to go on, the corners of her mouth turned up, if only for a second. It worked; Patrick could always lighten her up with his understanding and acceptance.

"You came for answers and all I can give you are more questions...."

Linda laughed out loud. "Questions? Hey! That's my job...all I do is ask questions...."

"And eventually you will have some answers," Patrick smiled into his cup. "But they might not be the answers you expect, right?

"Not to change the subject, or anything, but I've been meaning to tell you. I am transferring to North Chester Elementary and I have recommended you for my Vice Principal position. Congratulations!"

"Oh Patrick, I am so happy for you and so sad for me. What will I do without you here to talk to? Uh! And what's wrong with me? Thank you, Patrick. And thank you for appreciating and acknowledging my contribution. I guess that's an answer of sorts, isn't it?" Linda fleetingly smiled at her friend, but her expression refused to modify her mood.

Picking up a bottle of wine to celebrate her anticipated promotion she headed to her mother's to share the news. Betty met her at the door and looked troubled. "It might be a good idea to take Pom to the vet and have her pups delivered there. I don't like the way she looks."

Linda's short-lived enthusiasm vanished as she pushed past her mother and found Pom curled up in a position that spoke to how much pain she was in. Leaving Kelly with her Aunt Marion, Linda headed to the vets. It didn't take him long to determine Pom was in kidney failure. He told her he had to deliver the pups immediately or risk losing both Pom and her litter. Numb with fear, Linda nodded her approval.

During the surgery, Linda paced outside the vet's offices. She watched other owners bring their pets into the office then happily leave a few minutes later. She could not bear to see their joy, so she drove herself home to await the doctor's call.

Pacing back and forth Linda glared down at the telephone willing it to ring with good news from the vet. When that didn't work she moved to the window as if proximity to the outdoors would facilitate the delivery of her prayers to God to save her Pom. Filled with regret for the judgments she had had of God, she began to cut a deal.... "Dear God, I'll never question You again, just please save my pet. I'll quit smoking, drinking and swearing. From now on I'll really listen for Your wishes and obey them without question."

Unable to contain herself any longer, Linda picked up the phone. The nurse put her on hold. Linda held her breath to keep from shouting "Tell me, Godamnit, just tell me what's going on—"

"Linda?" the nurse's voice came back on the line.

"Y-yes?" OhpleaseGodplease.

"The doctor said he'll be with you in a moment...."

The news couldn't be good and it wasn't. Pom's pups were delivered, but the strain of the pregnancy had destroyed her kidneys.... "I'm afraid...."

Linda didn't hear the rest of the sentence; her mind was racing for some place, any place, to run. A dark quiet place where she didn't have to think, didn't have to watch, but most of all, didn't have to feel ANYTHING!

"...She's already under anesthesia," the vet continued. "It would be merciful to simply deepen her sleep...."

No! Her mind screamed. No! But her heart said you MUST! In spite of her grief and inescapable guilt she realized it was time to think about what Pom needed. This would be the most humane and caring gift of all. One she could provide Pom out of pure love...but would she have the courage and strength to let her go?

"...I'll need your permission...."

"No, nonononono." Did she say it or simply think it. "Wait; please wait until I can get there...." She hung up without waiting for his answer. Grabbing her car keys, she bolted out the door as she realized this would really be "goodbye."

Tears blurred her vision; her breath came in ragged, jagged gulps as she drove the short distance between her apartment and the veterinary hospital. Her mind continued to work on options for saving Pom. She cannot die! I will bring her home and nurse her back to health. It was my fault for letting Pom have another litter. But I was too afraid to have my loving companion spayed. It was my fault: I loved her too much; I didn't do enough; I've never done enough for my pets, my husband...myself. It was all my fault. Everything is all my fault. By the time she lost the argument with herself, she was parking in front of the vet's office.

Pom was curled up in a cage wrapped in warm terry cloth towels. Her limp body stirred slightly at the sound of Linda's voice. Seeing Pom's red blanket on the table Linda snatched it up and carried it to her cage. The black wires were in stark contrast to the overly bright white recovery room.

"C-can I hold her...." Linda was unlocking the cage before the vet's assistant could answer. Gently, oh so gently, she lifted her dying pet into her arms. "Thank you, Pom, thank you for waiting for me, my sweet child." Burying her face into her companion's soft black fur Linda began to weep. A low responsive moan escaped from Pom's throat. Linda reluctantly nodded her consent to the vet standing beside her.

He stepped forward, opened Pom's mouth and placed a tiny pill on the back of her tongue. It only took a moment for the little fur body to completely relax. The vet gently pulled her foreleg toward him and administered the sodium pentothal. Seconds later the room went still and Pom's spirit ascended into space where Arabeth awaited her arrival.

"Dear Linda, in the precise moment an animal passes over, one can sense and sometimes see the animal's aura depart as you have. Feeling so hopeless and helpless each soul mate desires to hold the connection as the animal spirit transitions. Together both souls are better served if they can find a way to celebrate the pet's life and departure. As the portal between worlds opens one can choose to believe this beloved soul lives on and that you have the free will to welcome her back into your life. In this moment of letting go, Pom needs your support to find the light and her soul guide on the other side.

"Linda, as an animal soul guide, I am the watchtower for my charges at the moment they change realities. So often I've witnessed the overwhelming fear, anger and grief humans can experience when their loving companions pass over. This loss can overshadow and temporarily make one forget the gratitude, trust and emotional vulnerability they were taught how to FEEL. The feeling depths these little ones touch and awaken are not always fully realized until 'good-byes' are said.

"The death of a pet can be a heart shattering experience, particularly when the relationship was grounded in unconditional love. Once they know this level of acceptance and trust the separation can be so devastating. Humans fear they will never recreate such closeness again. One can feel so empty.

"This is an opportunity for you to honor Pom's soul and give thanks for the short lived lives she and others agree to endure in order for

their humans to learn that death need not be an end to love. Linda you can become a role model for others to gain courage and self-worth through the experience of loss by opening to accept and survive the inevitable and repeated passing of all living beings in your life. Our beloved animals are skillful healers, here to serve us and prepare us to become whole within ourselves.

"I know this to be true, for I spent many lives on Earth as a human, until unconditional loving became my truth, my soul-connection to God and all living beings, and my celebrated birthright.

"Linda, you are not alone in your experience of grief and mourning. In my last human lifetime, I was a family lawyer, in a man's body. I saw much sadness in that lifetime and died in my early 40's from heart problems. I had come from a broken home, in a time when children were seen as objects without any rights. I chose the specialty of domestic law to defend and transform such devastating experiences for other children.

"My dearest friends and family worried I was too sensitive and emotional to be in this line of work yet I was so committed to the cause. When my wife was unable to have children we adopted two dogs. One was a mixed breed, collie / shepherd, the other a little poodle. Their soul-mated bond to each other was incredibly strong. They, in fact, became the children we would never have, as well as our best friends, for they taught us how to love each other in the same way. With great wisdom and compassion they helped me to know and experience unconditional love in the world. They gave me the hope and fortitude I needed to continue my work, seeing such unspeakable child abuse and neglect day after day. They died soon after me having completed their missions and brilliantly fulfilling our soul contract.

"When I reached the other side I was told that my earthly journey was successfully completed. My teacher gave me choices about what I wanted to do, in order to help other spirits find this wisdom. I asked to be trained as a spiritual guide to animals. I wanted to give back the love and compassion shown to me by my beloved dogs. So my spiritual training began. I chose a female body – I felt it would seem more nurturing for my animals. My first two 'little ones' were my own two dogs. I met them at the gate to the other side as they transitioned

over. Joy and tears flowed from all three of us as they ecstatically licked my face and neck. We knew we would be together forever. All three of us had finished our time on earth.

"Ever since it has become my sacred duty to help all animals grow and heal, so they can return to Earth and continue fulfilling their soul contracts with their humans. My charges stay with me until both human and animal are ready. Often I bring their human companions dreams to guide their process and paths back together.

"My dearest Linda, you are to know it was I who came from the other side to deliver your Pom to you. I was with her when she became ill after her puppies were born. I helped her through the physical body pain she experienced at her death and cradled her withered little body in my arms when we passed through the portal. It was then, that I placed her in her bed, fashioned after the one she loved so much on earth. It is here, with me, she will stay, to rest and rejuvenate, until YOU are ready to continue your soul mission's work with her."

The passing was so subtle; Linda didn't realize she was gone until the vet gently took Pom's body from her loving arms. The last thing Linda saw was the red corner of Pom's blanket as the vet carried her body through the swinging operating room doors. A few moments later, he returned and handed Linda the blanket. It was Friday, August 1st, 1975, a day Linda would never forget.

Not knowing how she made it home, Linda staggered into the empty apartment. She wondered if the tears would ever stop flowing, if her heart would ever stop breaking, if there were any reason to go on living her pain was so intense. Late afternoon sun slipped through the blinds creating stripes on the wooden floor. Linda noticed Pom's water bowl in the corner.

Crumbs from her last milk bone afloat on the surface. A new wave of grief threatened to overwhelm her. Still clutching Pom's blanket Linda entered her bedroom, threw herself onto her bed and tried to make sense of it all.

Tossing and turning, she longed for sleep... a deep dreamless sleep to obliterate all consciousness, all awareness, and all the memories associated with her pain. It may have been hours later when Linda pulled herself from the bed and stumbled into the bathroom. Reaching for the medicine cabinet door she stared at herself in the mirror. Rather than the pale face she was so used to seeing there were bloodshot blue eyes rimmed in red set into a face covered in angry crimson blotches. As if watching a stranger in the mirror she reached for a bottle of sleeping pills. Twisting the cap off she shook two into the palm of her hand. Hit with another wave of guilt she shook out several more and then the rest of the bottle into her moist palm. Her hand started to dissolve the little white pills. Quickly she poured a large glass of water. A ringing telephone broke the deafening silence. She paused glancing toward the sound then looked down at the pills melting in her palm. Breaking out of the comatose trance she threw them out of her hand and into the toilet, dashing for the phone.

"Hello?"

"Are you all right, Hon? It's Joe."

56

Chapter Six

The call from Joe saved Linda's life. It was as if Pom's spirit had inspired him to call her at that precise moment. Within minutes of hanging up, Linda heard a small voice from deep within her say, "You can kill yourself tomorrow, for tonight be at peace." She shook her head in amazement. "What was that?" But it made sense. She could get through tonight and not worry about tomorrow.

Joe surprised Linda by appearing on her doorstep that weekend. Their reunion was bittersweet: the pleasure of seeing each other was over-shadowed by the loss they shared. Joe suggested Linda return to Pope Air Force Base in North Carolina for a couple of weeks, to see where their relationship would lead them. No one understood the deep love and deeper loss that Pom's passing had had on Linda. No one but Joe.

As Linda packed for the trip, she glanced at her small library of fiction and non-fiction books on her intended-to-read-list. Now there was something she'd found of great interest that might take her mind off Pom. Her hand hovered for a moment, then settled on *Karmic Astrology: The Moon's Nodes,* by Martin Schulman; *Astrology and the Four Elements by Arroyo;* and *Saturn: A New Look at an Old Devil*, by Liz Green. She tossed them all into her suitcase.

After Joe dropped Kelly at Betty's house for the duration, he headed home. There he found Linda in the bedroom snapping the locks on her suitcase closed. Joe tried to lift it from the bed but immediately realized it was clearly heavier than he anticipated. "What do you have in here, bricks?"

Linda smiled, "No, Dear, just some 'light reading'."

Linda took those two weeks off even though Joe continued to work. After taking her morning walks Linda would settle in with the books she had brought along. Something fascinated her about karmic astrology although reading the daily horoscopes only added to her skepticism. She looked at it this way: For every one of the twelve sun signs there were millions of people born. How could approximately one twelfth of the world's population be having the same day every day? Then again, she had several satisfied friends who regularly consulted astrologers and paid handsomely for their services. What Linda did find consistently accurate was her sun sign's overview – Sagittarius had a passion for learning through travel and asking questions. She couldn't deny that she'd always had an overabundance of those.

The days passed by quite pleasantly. Joe's sweetness and devotion reminded her why she married him in the first place. Perhaps they had been siblings in a former life; they were so attuned to one another. Their unique connection was also nurtured by their desire to know the truth – another Sagittarian characteristic. Over time it was inevitable they would begin to share the previously secretive details of their time apart. In spite of their vows each of them had betrayed the relationship. Yet they found a way to forgive each other and make an attempt to salvage their marriage. At the end of the two weeks, Linda left Pope Air Force Base and went home to Baltimore after promising Joe she would accompany him on his next tour, wherever it was. He expected orders soon anyway and would let her know when and where he was going.

Linda's return to Baltimore that summer of 1973 infused her with a renewed sense of purpose for her work at Rosewood. Kelly remained at her mother's as she filled both her days and nights with work. When her associates inquired as to how she was recovering from Pom's loss, she smiled and brushed them off with her standard reply: "Fine." When in fact, she was anything but "fine." She did not want to talk about Pom's death even when her friends attempted to console her. Two of them had known Pom and loved her as well. Linda did not realize that they needed to talk about their feelings of grief and loss with her to help them heal too.

Having continued her studies in karmic astrology Linda quickly figured out why the newspapers' horoscopes were so unreliable...they were ridiculously over-simplified. This was a very complicated science, and art, requiring years of study to master. The sun wasn't the only planet of import! There were actually ten "planets" or significant planetary positions, twelve zodiac signs, twelve different house placements, and a series of rather mathematically intricate geometric aspects by which each planet-sign-house combination could be influenced. The combinations of possible outcomes, and therefore highly individualized interpretations, were exponentially staggering!

She learned that for centuries astrologers were the spiritual, educational and health care leaders in many ancient cultures. These accomplished ancient holistic practitioners had to be proficient mathematicians, astronomers, psychologists, linguists and communication specialists, to calculate and interpret the movement of heavenly bodies and ancient symbols in someone's natal chart.

Linda was a highly respected and intelligent educator who never took anyone's opinion as fact until she researched the subject at hand for herself. If she decided to become a practitioner and holistic teacher of karmic astrology, her colleagues and friends would surely benefit from this newly tapped source of ancient and esoteric wisdom. No longer did her day job provide answers to the "big" questions…it was her ever-blossoming passion for astrology that provided meaning and purpose in her life now.

After one particularly exhausting day, Linda fell into a fitful sleep. Appearing before her was a vaguely familiar woman wearing long, flowing white robes cradling Pom in her arms. All Linda could remember about the dream was what the woman said: "Your Pom needs you and will return to you shortly."

Feeling the tears slide from her eyes, Linda awakened in a rush of feeling that made her ache for her baby girl again. Could joy and grief co-exist in a single moment in time? Until then, Linda didn't think so, but today she was not so sure. Rolling over onto her side, she slipped back into a dreamless sleep unsure of what was real or imagined.

The next morning she got up with hope in her heart, which her mind quickly overruled. The thought of her Pom returning to her went beyond any rational thinking. And if Linda was anything, she was rational. Later that day, Joe called with his new orders: Hawaii it was!

Linda turned in her resignation and prepared to join her husband. Now, in February of 1977, with Pom gone and Kelly living in Baltimore County with her mother, the six month Hawaiian pet quarantine was inconsequential. Linda wondered if, perhaps, there was an energy force that guided their lives. If such intuitive knowing even existed, it was telling Linda her marriage to Joe was not yet over, by providing them with this fresh start. Maybe they had more "work" to do together....

Chapter Seven

When she first arrived in the islands, Linda loved taking long walks on the beach where the couple occasionally revisited their mutual indiscretions. "I knew when you lost that weight, I'd lose you...." Joe said, referring to the 72 pounds Linda lost before he went to the Philippines.

"But I'm back now—we're back. Aren't we?"

Joe didn't answer. Instead he turned her toward him, pulled her close to his body and enfolded her in his arms. She tried not to tense up and allow him to embrace her, but every feeling part of Joe sensed her lack of responsiveness. Reluctantly he released the pressure in his arms and let her go. "Take your time Hon, I can be patient," he conceded. "My orders in paradise are for two full years...let's make the best of them, OK?"

Linda nodded then turned east toward the water and the mainland. What was wrong now? Why was she unable to respond to his affection? What was it going to take to feel love for anyone ever again?

Some days the "aloha spirit" wrapped Linda in a warm and mellow environmental blanket. Long balmy, soft sensuous evenings seemed to be smothering the pain of Pom's death. Restful days helped create sleep-filled nights. Perhaps it was her beautiful surroundings or Linda's state of exhilaration as she immersed herself in her studies, but for the first time in her life she was content not working in her academic field. She wandered around quaint marketplaces finding interesting shells, crystals, Koa wood bowls, and more books on astrology.

After the initial blush of their reunion wore off, Joe returned to his work-filled military world and Linda disappeared into her self-guided study plan. The more she learned about astrology the more enraptured she became and the more she needed to know.

Linda was fascinated with the symbolic language of astrology. It reshuffled and wrapped previously unrelated terms and feelings together in ways that deepened her awareness of herself and others. Subtle shifts in human behavior were more understandable when underlying motivations and unmet needs were identified. On the surface "controlling" behavior didn't always feel the same – why was that? Virgo's want to set standards high and can be compulsively driven to make things "right" – they want to direct situations and people to create more perfect outcomes. Scorpio's fear is of being controlled, so they attempt to analyze and out maneuver people to feel powerful and diminish the possibility of being taken advantage of. Capricorn's believe they *know* what's "best" for others based on their experience, so they assume responsibility and control, to provide the most "beneficial" outcomes. Leo's want to be loved and acknowledged so they will do whatever it takes to stay in the limelight and keep your attention. Sensitive Pisces doesn't want to be alone and will use passive aggressive behavior to get what it needs. And so it goes...all of these energies can look and feel rather "controlling" but their motivations, behaviors and relationship styles are quite different. What insight! What brilliance! What wisdom this philosophy imparted!

The more Linda read, the more she appreciated why for centuries so many cultures had trusted astrology to explain a person's unique character pattern, developmental timetable and ways of experiencing the world. The symbolism of astrology added unlimited levels of dimension to understanding a person's character and potential.

She was also forming an appreciation for the role her soul played in her life and what it meant to feel connected to one's spiritual essence. Astrology was the ultimate divinational tool for translating the intersection between realities – those seen and conscious, versus those unseen, unconscious, and accessible by feelings, intuitions and visions. Yes! Linda now believed astrology was a credible metaphysical science of meaning and value. She believed the astrological chart was a spiritual roadmap, given to us by our souls. The chart's circular shape was divided into twelve (house) sections and depicted one's microcosm of the universal macrocosm. This unique snapshot of the heavens locates our solar system's planets, through which the twelve archetypal star constellations are orbiting, directly over a person's birthplace at the exact time of their delivery. These combinations of sign/planet/house energies symbolize all human experience. Like a reversed view of a satellite's global positioning system (G.P.S.), this divine scenario has God Positioning Souls to re-enter this mortal plane, with an encoded description of each soul's growth potential, in any given lifetime.

Interpreting this Sacred Mandala was an opportunity to hear our souls speak to us of our mind, body, spirit, and earthly senses using ancient symbols. Linda saw herself as a soul translator, using the client's astrological chart as her data source to help them navigate their earthly journey.

In truth, Linda was bringing forth her greatest gift and discovering her own purpose in this lifetime by becoming a karmic astrologer. Each individuated combination of symbols and house placements clearly demonstrated that everyone has a purpose – in fact, some people seem to be living their purpose without knowing a word of astrology. Or were they?

Linda made a habit of walking Bellows Falls beach in the early morning light. She was filled with so many new concepts and insights. The windward side of Oahu was lined with dark cypress trees that grew right up to the white sand line. Scorching heat from the tropical sun reflected onto the bottoms of her bare feet as her flip-flops swung from her hand. She thought she heard what sounded like a dog barking but questioned the possibility with the quarantine in effect.

Yes, it was a canine's voice she heard calling for help. Immediately her Pom came to mind. Damn! She'd come to Hawaii to renew the love she felt for Joe and once and for all leave behind the painful memory of Pom's loss. But her soul clearly had other plans. Instead, she seemed to be losing Joe and once again yearning for the love she had shared with her Pom.

Linda wondered how she'd feel when they returned to Baltimore and there were dogs everywhere. What was she thinking? Return to Baltimore? Joe still had another 18 months duty here after which he could be sent to Timbuktu, Europe, or Asia—anywhere, but not likely Baltimore.

The barking turned to a high pitched "yip." Linda whirled in an attempt to locate the source of the sound. She discovered a frightened shaggy mutt whose collar and tag trapped him beneath a fallen palm tree branch.

"There, there, little one we'll get you out." Quickly she stooped down and lifted the branch to free the struggling animal. Before she could stand up he scrambled into her lap, licked her face in apparent gratitude then dashed off toward base housing. The dog's tongue was covered with sand, which was now on

Linda's chin and cheek. Lifting her hand to her face she brushed it off. She was not surprised to discover tears there too. The recurrent pain, which had surfaced, reaffirmed her inability to escape Pom's memory anywhere in the world. She was still so wounded by the loss... much too hurt to conceive of having another pup in her life.

Observing this scene, Arabeth shook her head in sorrow, feeling compassion for Pom and how inconsolable he seemed.

"There, there little one—she'll change her mind and then you can come back to her a happier, healthier companion. She has begun to long for the Divine nature of love and loving that you brought into her life. You'll have the opportunity to be with your girl again. She just needs more time."

That night she told Joe what he already knew. Whatever hope they had for repairing their marriage had died along with Pom. If they couldn't make the union work in paradise, it didn't stand a chance anywhere else. With resignation and sadness Linda promised to take care of the legalities. Joe promised to stay in touch.

Back in Baltimore, Linda responsibly, but half-heartedly, resumed her work at Rosewood. There was so much to do, yet her heart wasn't in it. Since her absence the *Baltimore News American* had published an exposé called the "Agony behind the Acacias." The beauty of the facility's Georgian architecture did not extend inside its walls where the hellish living conditions of the mentally and physically challenged children were no longer tolerable. As an educator and administrator Linda recommitted with resolve to improve this situation or die trying. Perhaps this was her lot in life if no longer her passion. Maybe this was preparation for doing her soul mission.

Now as vice principal Linda spent less time with patients and more time managing staff and functions. She gave 110% to her day work while continuing her astrological studies at night. For the next seven years, Linda was all work and no play – a life style she had learned well from her mother. It was her study of astrology that kept her connected to her soul. Slowly her love of astrology began to evolve into a private part-time practice. At least her free time was consumed with something she loved.

Chapter Eight

The day Michael entered Linda's life initially seemed quite uneventful. For months she had known that on September 13, 1980, her chart indicated a strong potential for meeting her soul mate. The planet Saturn was going to conjunct her soul mission's north node in the house of relationships, an event that would occur in her chart only once every thirty years. Saturn asks us to assume responsibility for aspects of our lives in which we need to develop and mature...to reframe old habits and patterns that no longer serve our highest good and go beyond the limitations of our minds. All day she paid attention to the people she attracted into her life. Nothing happened. No one new or interesting appeared. Just the same faces coming and going through her day.

After a while she simply stopped noticing as she prepared to leave for a two-week vacation to Disneyworld with her niece Carrie. Linda had only one more thing to do. She wanted to say goodbye to her principal. A hippie-looking guy, Michael Brady, sat in the secretary's office waiting for his interview. Seriously overdressed with long hair and a full beard, Michael wore a large leather bag on his shoulder. He looked so out of place in that environment, Linda's first reaction was to stifle a smile.

She walked past him into the principal's office. "Who is that guy waiting for you?"

"Probably our new psychologist," Mayer laughed.

"Great!" Linda's reaction was a frown. One of her duties as Vice Principal was to conduct the orientation and training of all new psychologists. They came and went with regularity due to the conditions at the school and their own career objectives. She assumed he would be another in a long line of ambitious newly minted shrinks.

Later that day while cruising through North Carolina, her niece asked, "Well, did you meet him today?"

"Who him?" Linda replied.

"You KNOW. Your soul mate...remember your chart said...."

That'll teach me to rely on predictive astrology, Linda thought wryly. Then she remembered Michael. He was the only new guy she had met that day, but he was certainly not her soul mate. Not her type at all – too young, too married and she was going to wind up supervising him.

Upon her return from Florida, Linda began Michael's orientation program. His work ethic and open heart pleasantly surprised Linda. He turned out to be a conscientious worker, energetic team player and not too proud to roll up his sleeves and get his hands dirty. Linda developed respect for his willingness to help her students. She learned he was not only married but had recently become the father of a baby boy. But the best surprise of all was his interest in her passion – astrology. When he learned Linda instructed students in astrology, Michael enrolled in her entry level class.

It wasn't long before Michael and Linda were regularly taking their lunch hours together to discuss life's big issues. Bright, articulate and fun, Michael entertained Linda without any danger of involvement, or so she thought. Then again, John Lennon may have had more wisdom on the subject when he wrote, "Life is what happens when you have other plans."

In spite of her self-defined relationship taboos, Linda found herself rather attracted to the young psychologist. This presented a host of problems. Becoming interested in a married man was compromising enough without the added dimension of being co-workers at Rosewood. The institution had barely survived the last round of scandals.

As their friendship progressed Michael confided in Linda that his marriage was becoming intolerably claustrophobic. He had already informed his wife of his need to spend a weekly night out to pursue his own interest in astrology. As a trained psychologist, he approached the subject from a holistic point of view as had Carl Jung, which complemented Linda's broad conceptual perspective.

Linda felt so comfortable with him it seemed as if they had known each other before. "Perhaps in a former life?" Michael quipped. Linda smiled in recognition.

One evening Betty cornered her daughter for some advice concerning her own marital relationship with Linda's stepfather. He was an untreated alcoholic who was becoming continually more abusive. Her mother needed to leave him but didn't know how. This placed Linda in an awkward position, so she recommended that Michael provide her with professional and objective advice. Michael gladly volunteered to help out and agreed to meet Betty at Linda's apartment to guarantee her privacy.

After three hours of intense emotional work Betty felt prepared to face her husband and headed home. Linda had unobtrusively observed Michael throughout the counseling session. She had watched him work before but this time was taken with his incisive and intuitively sensitive approach to her mother's dilemma. Something shifted in her that evening portending a change in their relationship – their bond had become more than a friendship. As a "thank you" for Michael's generous intervention Linda insisted on taking him to dinner. When they returned to her apartment, they both realized their intellectual and emotional intimacy was no longer enough. Against their better judgment they made love.

Linda knew the importance of keeping their relationship a secret. Quite satisfied that her mother had received the help she needed, Linda glanced at her chart one more time before putting it away. A sense of darkness enveloped Linda's heart. She recognized a problematic aspect that typically forced unwanted change into a person's life.

Two weeks later Betty entered the hospital with a blood clot in her leg. Within the week she was diagnosed with liver cancer.

The void. Limbo. Purgatory. Linda didn't know what to call it. "Hell" came to mind but seemed too dramatic. Watching her mother die while loving Michael in secrecy was a surreal experience. He had left his wife and was now living with Linda but no one could know. Both of their positions would be compromised if the relationship became common knowledge or began to impact their professional effectiveness. How could she have let this occur? The longer she lived the more complicated life got!

Outside of Rosewood Linda spent every spare moment with her nose buried in an astrology book, or poring over a chart, or counseling one of her many new clients. They came to her with an endless string of questions knowing her insights would create more conscious awareness, clarity and focus in their lives.

The alarm vibrated her out of a deep sleep she really did not want to leave. For a fleeting moment she fantasized how good it would be to have a dog that needed to be walked. She saw Pom's face in her mind's eye before consciousness shoved her back into reality. Even now, years after her passing, tears still formed in recognition of her companion's absence. Never having completed the grieving process for Pom, she feared her mother's death would just open up all her wounds once again. How would she ever learn to accept the loss of loved ones when the void they created seemed excruciating? How would she be able to handle her mother's death if she couldn't deal with her dog's passing? Thank God Michael was there to lean on this time! With Michael's love and skillful support Linda began to actively grieve Betty's impending loss. Due to the work she had done with Michael, her mother's death on the Winter Solstice of 1980 brought a sense of relief instead of anguish. Linda was stunned and grateful as her burden lifted. Still unable to address the death of her beloved Pom at least she was emotionally prepared for Betty's funeral. What her friends and co-workers hadn't known was clearly revealed at graveside – Michael and Linda were deeply in love.

Three months later one glorious spring morning, Linda was adjusting the volume on her car radio as she balanced a cup of hot coffee against the steering wheel. Out of thin air, but as clear as a bell she heard her mother's voice shout, "Linda, what exactly are you waiting for? I've provided you with the means and you continue to do the same old thing….Rosewood is your history, it's time to create your future!"

Caught off guard Linda jerked the wheel to her right, almost scorching herself with coffee. "What means?" Her modest inheritance had been put into savings. Perhaps Betty meant she should live on it until she figured out what to do next? She almost turned the car around to consult her books and chart but her sense of responsibility overrode that impulse. OK! It was time to listen to her mother's advice. She made a decision to act on that impulse before she slipped back into her old safe habits. The next day she gave Rosewood her resignation letter and three weeks later an anxious but highly energized Linda drove off the Rosewood compound for the last and final time.

Leaping into the void she expected a symbol from the universe to direct her. In the meantime, while she awaited guidance, she would become a full-time practitioner of the art and metaphysical science of astrology.

An ad in the classifieds caught her eye. Was this the signal she'd been waiting for? There was a small store available for lease nearby. Michael resigned from Rosewood to join her in the practice. Selling everything she could turn into cash, including the sports car that she loved, Linda and Michael opened a book store in historic Reisterstown, Maryland, called

Aquarius Rising.   She used the proceeds from everything liquidated to create inventory. Behind a sagging front porch the old Victorian house had two rooms. Linda packed the first with metaphysical books, herbs and art objects, some of which were on consignment. The back room provided space for astrology consultations and small classes. The antique stores surrounding Aquarius Rising provided a good bit of drop in traffic. It was fun while it lasted but did not produce enough income to support the two of them. They closed the shop and moved her practice into their two-bedroom apartment.

Linda's practice grew through referrals as her reputation for uncanny insights and predictions delivered more and more clients to her door. She developed new curriculums for teaching astrology classes to her clients who wanted to know more about this highly unique database of personal history and soul potential information. During one of those classes she was explaining the impact of a difficult transit in her life. Linda told her story of Pom's passing.

What was she talking about? What did she mean? I ran and got my teacher Arabeth, to help me understand. I thought I'd died when I needed to and would return to continue my work with Linda when she was ready.

My teacher and I watched as Linda explained her fear of having me spayed, and that I had died after having a litter of puppies that Linda believed I should never have become pregnant with.

Oh Linda, how can you still blame yourself so? Do you not yet believe everything happens for a reason and is "perfect" in every moment? That the real growth occurs through our pain and times of crisis to show us what we need to see about ourselves or remember? As incredibly useful as astrological chart information is, even good astrologers need an objective translator to gain insights into their own unconscious. She was so terrified to go through the loss of another dog she truly believed it would destroy her instead of create healing. She told her class that night that she had even tried to kill herself after I had passed over. Then she said what I never thought I would hear. She said SHE WOULD NEVER HAVE ANOTHER ANIMAL SHARE HER LIFE AGAIN. First I was numb! Then I started to shake and whimper. Arabeth picked me up and hugged me tight until I could stop shaking. "Is it true, is it true? Can Linda choose not to have me back?"

Arabeth turned to me and said "Little one, Linda can make that choice; she does have free will. She would have to be awfully brave to overcome her pain, and guilt, and fear. Wouldn't she?"

I thought about all that. Yet all I knew was how much I loved Linda and how much she had loved me. "Arabeth? It's really not in me to be afraid of love. I need another chance to teach her that!"

Arabeth explained, "I know dear one, but humans are still learning about what you already know to be true. You see humans come to earth with the same expectations of being unconditionally loved by God and their souls, as you and I already possess. As their lives begin, they find love is only available to them when they meet certain conditions, or behave in particular ways that are expected of them. The experience, of not being loveable enough for who they innately are, begins to shatter their trust in the world – in others – and eventually in themselves. They are desperate to regain this womb-like loving heart-connection without which the world becomes a fearful place. Instinctively they find ways to protect themselves from feeling the agony and separation experienced when love is withdrawn or withheld. "Their journey through many incarnations becomes focused on regaining feelings of self-respect, unconditional acceptance, worthiness and love. Yet, most humans only become motivated to shift their fear-based foundations back to one of love when their souls face challenges or crises that disrupt their lives. Then they are motivated to prioritize and direct their attention to what is causing them pain.

"This is the most important reason they need animals in their lives. Animals can face anything even their own deaths when they unconditionally love another being. Also animals understand the cycle of life - AND accept it. They instinctively know the soul lives on. Linda needs your help to 'remember' that".

"Arabeth, can I be of service to her from up here? Can I help her find the courage to love a dog, and herself, again? It's my job, isn't it?"

Arabeth looked lovingly at me for quite a long while. "You know what? I think we can. Soon, we will go to Linda in a dream and touch her heart in a way that will help her know how incomplete her life is without your love in it."

"Thank you, Arabeth, thank you."

Chapter Nine

Michael found work at a psychiatric hospital but earning only enough money to support his son and ex-wife. This motivated Linda to become the couple's primary bread-winner and maintain an active practice.

One evening after months of all work and no play, Michael felt like a vacation was in order. "How about a road trip? I have some mental health time to take, so consult your charts and tell me where we should go for a break."

Amid her books, charts and client folders, Linda pulled out her own chart and checked the ephemeris for the best dates to travel and most energetically favorable locations.

"How about Maine?" Michael suggested. "Or Massachusetts... Vermont... anywhere but Ocean City or the south...."

Linda noted a disturbing transit in her chart. "Looks like Mars is doing a tap dance on me for the next several weeks...not a good aspect in the whole chart."

"All the more reason to split town...." Michael slid his arms around her waist and pulled her to him. "Bar Harbor?"

"Sure," Linda smiled, "why not?"

Why not, indeed. Linda drove most of the trip because she loved to drive and covered the 1000 miles in record time. They checked into a motel and spent several days seeing the sights and enjoying their little escape from reality, clients and patients.

One sunny morning Michael suggested renting some mopeds for a trip up the coastline. It had been years since Linda had ridden a bike but her adventurous Sagittarian spirit would not pass up this opportunity for such fun outdoors on such a beautiful day.

The first five minutes on the moped almost killed her. Her legs wouldn't stop wobbling and the steering wheel apparently had a mind of its own. Nonetheless, Linda maneuvered the narrow street barely in control when a car careened around the corner and into her lane. She instinctively over-corrected the direction of the moped, hit the curb, and was thrown to the pavement. Never one to give up, she sprang to her feet, pulled down her shirt and got back on the vehicle. Now feeling more confidence, she was flying down the road ahead of Michael when her front wheel hit a patch of loose gravel catapulting her body off the bike and onto the adjacent embankment. In less than a second her own moped hit her from behind and slammed her into the ground. Her mind flashed to her chart, having seen the possibility of her own death. That was the last thought she had before her head hit the solid ground and she lost consciousness.

When she came to, a pale and shaken Michael was bent over her. His voice trembled as he tested her consciousness trying to get her to tell him what hurt. Slowly he helped her get up and led her toward the driver of a car who had seen the accident and stopped to help.

Back at the hotel, Linda went right to bed, determined to sleep off the pain wracking her right side. At 4 AM it became apparent she needed medical attention. At Michael's insistence they went to the emergency room at the local hospital. There she discovered the damages: collapsed right lung, three broken ribs and damaged nerves in her right arm. For 24 hours Linda was forced to stay in the hospital until her lung inflated at which point she insisted Michael drive her back to Baltimore.

As soon as they arrived home, Marion called to tell them that Kelly had passed away in his sleep. He had died on the same day that Linda had had her accident. Linda was so numb from pain and medication that this information barely registered and the single tear that rolled down her cheek went unnoticed.

While recovering Linda had plenty of time to replay the accident and her foreknowledge of it. She realized her nagging doubts were not about her astrological practice but the predictive nature of it. She had predicted this life altering accident yet knew that at some level, she had to experience it – she just wasn't clear why! Perhaps predicting her clients' lives caused them to avoid experiences they needed to have…perhaps she was robbing them of lessons needed for their spiritual growth…usurping critical learnings on their path and interfering with their soul's divine plan.

Recovering from the accident provided Linda with plenty of time to study karma. It helped her make sense of why she was aware of the imminent danger and yet exposed herself to the pain and trauma anyway. Her soul had presented her with other opportunities to investigate the subject of karma, but she had not listened. Sometimes it took a lot to get Linda's attention especially if it meant delving into her own unconscious. But she was beginning to realize her soul would always have the last word. Linda's lesson was clear: she did not have the right, nor did she want the responsibility of re-directing another's soul path using predictive astrology. How would any of her clients ever take responsibility for their own creations if they could blame someone else for not having given them enough, or too much, information?

She began questioning her very deepest beliefs. She wasn't sure she understood the concept of self-fulfilling prophecies: were people capable of changing their futures by putting out intent? The accident taught her that to be a karmic astrologer she had to respect free will and creative choice. Perhaps the accident was a bizarre message from her soul to get her attention.

The more she studied Jung, Cayce and Schulman the more convinced she became of her mission: she was to be a karmic astrologer and new age philosopher. The accident was the threshold she had to pass through to crack open the door to this awareness and step into her future of research and teaching. Her mother's whispered encouragement gave her the support she needed to never look back!

This was it – this was the window of opportunity Pom and I had waited for! Linda was open to a new way of living. The accident had opened her mind and heart to the power of symbols, serendipity and listening to one's own intuition. She had studied what Carl Jung called "Synchronicity". Linda thought she understood the concept but now she had actually experienced the miracle of listening to and recognizing her soul's messages. This is what was meant by "conscious living" and "being in the moment"! She trusted her soul to know what she needed and when. This was it! So simple! So brilliant! So exquisitely perfect! "Serendipity" and "Synchronicity" was HOW LIFE HAPPENED, when we allowed our souls, and God, to guide us on our journey, when we found the wisdom to stop over-controlling our own lives and outcomes. Our job was only to distill and extract the meaning of what showed up in our space. For all things, in every moment, we're our soul's, and God's, creation! All opportunities and potential learnings – presented to each soul on its path to enlightenment – occur at exactly the most perfect moment. Each moment becomes a crossroads of choice for our personality or our soul to make. Either path taken, eventually, would lead us to the lesson our soul intended us to create! If the divine soul choice were not accepted, there would be other opportunities, and lifetimes, to choose it.

This was the perfect time to send Linda Pom's dream.

That evening Linda dreamed about a woman that she recognized from years before. She visualized Arabeth as neither young nor old, with a timeless quality. She had short blonde hair and deep blue eyes. She was plump with full breasts, dressed in a long toga of pale blue with silver trim, full sleeves, no shoes, small pearl earrings and no other jewelry. Her energy was welcoming, mothering and emotionally sensitive. Her eyes sparkled yet Linda could see the depths of sadness and pain she was capable of that could bring up tears of empathy.

In the dream Arabeth speaks:

"Linda, your Pom needs your help. Look at him. His little black and white body and soul are imprisoned in a metal cage on the upper floor of a building. He will not be released until you pay his ransom of $387.50."

Chapter Ten

My teacher and I took our last walk together to the portal that would lead my soul back to earth and my girl. She held me so gently in her arms; I couldn't kiss her sweet face enough. I knew we would meet again, but it was so hard to say good-bye. With one last look at doggie heaven I blinked my eyes and found myself in a metal cage, shivering with cold, trying to find my earth mother's tit. This mother was so frail unlike my last doggie mother. Before I felt so warm and comfortable after my delivery. My mommy was healthy and well cared for. The humans were always there to help her and all of us pups.

Now it is different. My little puppy heart went out to her as I lay quietly among my other littermates. We would have to be strong to live through all this. Three of my brothers and sisters didn't make it – there wasn't enough milk for all of us. I knew they were going to the other side to be with their teachers. I wished them well. My earth mother just couldn't handle that pregnancy. It wasn't too long after that she passed on too. She had just had one litter after another until her body couldn't take it any longer. I was happy for her because she too would be going home to that beautiful restful place I had just left. Now I needed to have patience. I knew Linda would find me. She had to find me. I had to trust what I believed.

I was flown in one of those airplanes to a store, put into a cage and permanently kept there. People would come by and stare at me. I would pretend I was angry or stubborn, like Taurus the bull, so no one would connect with me – or want me. This prison was to be my home until Linda rescued me. My only job was to stay healthy and keep watching for my girl. Everyday was the same as the day before. I'd jump up and look around, even though I couldn't see anything more than a few feet beyond my cage door.

Linda moaned in her sleep loud enough to awaken Michael.

"What's wrong, Honey? Wake up...you're dreaming."

Michael's baritone voice dragged Linda back into consciousness.

"Pom-Pom's in trouble."

"Who? What? Honey, Pom's gone. She died nine years ago...."

"No! She came to me in a dream. He was in a cage...."

"Linda, I thought you told me Pom was a girl...."

"She was, only this time she's a he...and he's black and white and in a black metal cage. A woman told me he'd been kidnapped and is being held on the second floor—and his ransom is $387.50." Linda's voice broke with the retelling of her dream.

"Okay...okay, I believe you," he lied.

Two weeks later Linda and Michael were shopping at the Golden Ring Mall in East Baltimore. Uncharacteristically she found herself dragging Michael into the pet shop. "But you hate these places! You hate these puppy factories. Why are you torturing yourself like this?" Michael stared at her in disbelief. They were standing between rows of black wire cages on the second floor of a pet store in a Mall. Linda stood as if listening to a faraway voice. Michael started toward the door to leave. Behind Linda, Pom was jumping up and down and barking. Linda didn't seem to notice. And then, as if pulled by an invisible string, Linda circled back for one last look. Michael watched her turn toward the cage and look inside at the busy bundle of black and white fur flinging itself up against the cage. He shook his head and sighed.

"Please, can we take this one out to play with?" Linda asked a nearby clerk.

"Certainly," the clerk opened the cage door and Pom flew from the enclosure right into Linda's arms. Pom licked her chin, cheeks, neck, ears, and hands. Linda began to cry though her tears were kissed away before they fell from her face. Shaking his head, Michael recognized his cue. "How much to take the puppy home?"

"$500...but that includes a bed, training crate and—"

Michael abruptly interrupted, "It could include a month's worth of pet food but it's still too much to pay for a dog." Michael touched Linda's elbow signaling that it was time to go home. "C'mon, Hon...."

Linda clutched the puppy tighter. "There's something wrong...my dream was explicit $387.50...and I know this is the dog, I can feel it...." She turned around visually scanning the interior space of the pet store. "Everything else is the same...the second floor of the mall, the cage, everything but the price...."

"I don't know why you want to complicate our lives with a dog anyway...we don't have time to train it, our budget doesn't have the room to include it, and...."

"And it's a he, not an it. Including a puppy in our lives enriches...."

"Poverty is hardly enrichment…." Michael muttered then stepped back from Linda and the puppy.

Linda looked up, confusion still contorting her face. "My dream, in my dream he was going to cost $387.50." She couldn't understand why everything else in the dream made sense but this.

"See? That means we aren't supposed to get this one…that's the message." Michael turned his back and firmly motioned Linda to follow him from the store.

"Excuse me please; are you interested in that dog?" A more mature voice intruded on the scene. The manager approached them with a smile. "He is a very special dog," she said in her best sales voice. Overhearing the manager's comment Michael turned around. "For five hundred dollars worth of dog he'd better clean up after himself," Michael snapped.

"You are the first one he's taken to – usually we can't keep Shih Tzu's in the store because of their adorable look and temperament, but this one has been a little difficult," she said. She reflected on the bared teeth and raised ruff whenever someone approached his cage. That was his behavior until Linda arrived. The manager had never seen him so friendly or so close to being sold.

"I'll say," contributed the clerk. The manager shot her a look. The clerk backed out of the conversation and moved away from them.

"See? You'd have us pay $500 for someone else's problem, Hon?" said a disgusted Michael.

"Oh no!" The manager cut in, "He's just $387.50—-you only need to cover my costs to date...."

Linda gave Michael "the look." Michael rolled his eyes and pulled out his wallet. Flipping through the cash, he shook his head. There was no arguing now!

"We can give you a down payment, but we'll have to come back with the rest." It was Saturday; the banks were closed, so it would be Monday before the dog could come home with them.

Linda clutched Pom closer with the news of the delay.

"Monday works fine—it will give me a chance to get the papers in order."

Linda cried uncontrollably on the way home.

"Now what is it?" Michael's tone indicated he was losing patience. "You found the dog, and you'll get him on Monday."

"You don't understand.... I am so afraid of losing him."

"Losing him? You haven't even brought him home yet! What is there to lose?" He slammed on the brakes in exasperation.

"Honey, I lost him once and it hurt so much I've been unable for years to allow an animal into my heart. My dream led us to him, and he IS the right dog, I just know it...but I'm almost paralyzed with fear now that I've found him, I won't be able to bring him home. Perhaps a fire in the store, accidental poisoning, or—"

Michael reached across the front seat and grabbed Linda's wrist. "Trust me on this, Hon. You know I really don't even want a dog but I know this is the dog for you…and I'll bring him home on Monday. That's my promise to you." Linda squeezed his hand, and turned to look out the window to avoid showing her husband the doubt and fear behind her eyes.

Pom couldn't believe Linda had left him. Had he done something wrong? Had Linda decided that she didn't want him back? He moved to the back of his cage, flopped down with his head between his paws and created a mind picture to connect to Arabeth.

"No, dear one, you did not fail her. You did exactly what she needed you to do. The pain she felt with your passing and the courage she found in herself to love your soul again has unchained a part of her soul. You taught her never to let the fear of being hurt overcome her desire to love. It was YOU, little one, who showed her how truly painful living WITHOUT love could be - especially without the love of SELF. YOU did that for your Linda. And that's not all. Remember the time you were so impulsive you jumped off the balcony? Well, that may have scared her but it also taught her something about her own impetuosity. She learned that type of behavior hurts the people we love. She had done similar things to Joe. Your impetuousness, your risk-taking, your strong need to be active and in motion - all of those are Arian traits. You taught her every day that Aries was who you were. She had never thought about astrology until then. Watching you and realizing how true you were to your sun sign created her first credible exposure to astrology. In time she learned that astrology was to become her truth because of what YOU set in motion. She found her passion and became an astrologer because of you. She is learning about souls and soul connections because of you. You have given her such gifts!"

Pom goes to sleep knowing Arabeth is right. Linda will come back and get him.

Saturday and Sunday were sleepless nights for Linda. She hustled Michael out the door as soon as the bank opened on Monday. She saw the client that she had scheduled for that day. A half a pack of cigarettes later, she heard the sound of their car pulling into the space before their building. Racing to the door, she threw it open and rushed out to the car.

"Welcome home, my Pom...."

Grabbing the car door she flung it open and leaned in to pull Pom's cage toward her. Fingers trembling she opened the door to the crate and urged the puppy to her. "Come here baby...Pom, it's so good to see you again." Lifting the dog to her chest, she felt her heart center open meeting the love emanating from his warm body – this reunion had taken almost a decade to achieve.

Once inside the house, Michael placed the empty crate on the floor, stood to the side and observed his wife's affection for the puppy. "Pom, Pom, Pom...."Linda murmured into the dog's soft furry neck.

"Uh, no. I'll go along with your theory of how he got here, because I don't have another explanation—but Pom was a Pekinese AND a girl, for God's sakes!

"You're right, Michael." Linda placed the puppy in his crate, and then yanked the paperwork from the top. Opening it, she skimmed the print, and then looked up at her husband. "Yes, he's a Taurus—Born May 1ˢᵗ, 1984 in Kansas City, Kansas. Pom was pure Aries – the earthy Taurian influence will calm his fiery Aries ego. Shih Tzu's are from Tibet—the home of Buddha. He's loyal and loving…and patient." She looked up at Michael and smiled.

Inside the crate, the pup was on his hind legs doing a dance hoping to get Linda's attention so that she would take him out again. She looked at him lovingly. "Wonder why he returned as a Shih Tzu?"

"It means Lion in Chinese," Michael laughed. "A great big name for such a little dog."

"Leo? Should we call him Leo, as in Lion? That's my North Node.   Linda realized, "Oh my God, he is here to help me achieve my soul mission in Leo! "

"Sure, we can name him Leo if you want me to laugh every time I look at him…."

"How about Tai Chi—energy, dance, movement…That's it, we'll name him Tai Chi.

Chapter Eleven

Months before, Linda had planned a trip to Spain to find her past. She knew that going to that country would provide important answers to her deep seated fears. When she had made the reservations, she could not have anticipated that Pom's soul would have chosen that time to return to her. She was terribly conflicted.

Distraught, Linda hunched over Tai on their living room sofa. Her shoulders shook, tears flowed freely and her body enfolded the black and white bundle of fur.

"Linda, please…this is ridiculous!" Michael paced in front of them.

"I cannot leave him now. Not yet." Her voice cracked between the words.

"No! You WILL not leave him—it's not that you CAN'T, you won't. And I can't help but wonder if you love that damned dog more than you...."

"Stop it. That has nothing to do with it...."

"Then what? It wasn't my idea to buy a dog a few days before our trip to Spain—and while we're on the subject, it wasn't MY idea to go to Spain—of all the countries in Europe worth visiting, Spain would be the last one on my list. It gives me the creeps every time I see the Running of the Bulls. Why in the world would we choose a country for a vacation when it takes pride in turning cruelty into a sport?" He sputtered out of breath before all the words he had to say were said.

"Michael, you know how important this trip is for me...."

"And you know we can't afford to go, so...."

"That's why I sold the diamond Mother left me. I know my karma lies there. I know I have past lives there. My Mars in Scorpio is in the ninth house, and Pluto is preparing to enter Scorpio – it means I am about to go through a major transformation. I need to be in Spain to see what lessons Pluto has in store for me...."

"For you! " Michael pouted.

"And for my clients! How can you expect me to help my clients if I can't help myself by facing my own demons?" Linda looked down at Tai snuggled into her arms. "My tears are for you, little one. I know I have to go on this trip but...."

"Jesus Christ!" Michael shouted, stomped from the room, slamming the door behind him. "He's a dog, a dog, for God's sakes!" The closed door between them muffled Michael's voice.

The empty suitcases lay open in front of Linda. She was physically unable to pack them. She pulled a drawer out so far it fell on the floor narrowly missing her feet. "Damnit!" she said, stooping over and picking it up, then throwing it on the floor next to the open suitcase. Grabbing two fistfuls of underwear she dropped them into the bag. Tai scooted from beneath the bed and tried to catch a bra on its way down. Missing the cup with his mouth, the strap lassoed his neck, startling him and sending him back beneath the bed pulling the slingshot behind him. In spite of herself, Linda laughed. The sound of her voice lured him out into the open. He happily scurried into her open arms. Drawing him close, she felt his fast beating heart. "Tai, Tai—I just found you and now I'm going to leave you again." She started to cry again. "You must promise me you'll be all right – you will be safe... and…" Tai stretched his neck upwards and licked her face until it was void of tears. He had promised!

What was going on? Linda couldn't regain her focus or composure. Her anxiety level continued to escalate. If she didn't know any better she would have sworn this was a panic attack of sorts. One foot in front of the other… that was the best she could do at the moment. She picked up her packing list and began organizing. Finishing the task gave her the excuse she needed to ask Michael to drive Tai to the client's house who volunteered to dog sit. First checking and rechecking the tickets, she pulled their passports out, then counted the traveler's checks. As Michael pulled the car out of the driveway Linda became dizzy and felt a wave of nausea go through her stomach. Racing to the bathroom, there was nothing left to eject. Just dry heaves. Michael recognized an anxiety attack when he saw one. Linda's physical symptoms certainty confirmed the significance and degree of emotional trauma that even temporary separation from her pet could create. As a psychologist he realized he needed an attitude adjustment. He couldn't be of any support or help to her if he couldn't get some perspective on the situation.

Once on the plane, Linda became totally silent. No words were exchanged for a half-hour until Michael was unable to take it any longer. He took her hand in his and leaned over to get her attention. "Hon, you've traveled all of your life. Tai marched right into Jane's house as if he owned the place...he seemed to know you'd come back and get him. Honest. And the plane is not going to crash...we were in more danger driving to Friendship Airport than flying to Spain...."

Linda turned and stared at him. Her blue eyes rimmed in red, her face catatonically devoid of expression. "I know."

Michael sighed heavily. "Then, what is it?"

"I...don't... know." She turned away and returned to her vigil.

Costa del Sol was their first stop on the two-week trip. This vacation Mecca may have been known to the world as the "Sun Coast" but Linda and Michael only experienced rain, cold temperatures and dreary weather – hardly the warm, sunny Spain they had read about in the travel brochures. It was fitting somehow since the weather mirrored Linda's mood. As soon as the plane landed she raced to the phone to call and check on Tai. The report was good but it did little to lighten her frame of mind. Fear and anxiety engulfed her every moment. Michael attributed her reactions to jet lag. Linda knew it was much more than that.

Finally the weather broke and Michael and Linda made dinner plans at a beach side restaurant. Following the waiter's suggestion they ordered a pitcher of the local Sangria. Again, Michael reached for Linda's hand trying to connect with her. Suddenly, the restaurant's lights went out. They sat in total darkness. Only the sound of waves rhythmically beating the shoreline penetrated the thick humid air. It felt like a womb to Linda as she inhaled deeply to create more space for herself and shake off her claustrophobic sense of the room. She was lost in her thoughts…elusive thoughts that had been playing on the edges of her consciousness for days. The lights flickered on, dimmed, and then came back up again, illuminating the shocked expression on Linda's face.

"Michael! I remember—can we cancel tomorrow's bus trip?"

Michael immediately felt the shift in Linda's gloom. "What?"

At first Michael was reluctant to alter the plans they had knocked themselves out to make. They were scheduled to go on a three-day tour of the Spanish countryside. Then again Linda was not one to offhandedly discard plans or waste hard-earned money. Instinctively he knew not to question her suggestion. He agreed to fly to Madrid first thing the next morning.

"My journey begins here," Linda mumbled as they climbed the steps into the Prado, Spain's premier art museum. Michael was so grateful and relieved that Linda's mood had lightened; he followed her inside reserving his questions for later.

Briskly moving from floor to floor Linda behaved as if she was searching for something, something she'd recognize. Michael paused in front of a large painting of a hunt scene from the 17th century.

"Michael! Over here…."Linda exclaimed. Her shocked voice contained both confirmation and fear. She stood frozen in place with her index finger pointing at the portrait of a family of Spanish royalty with their retinue of servants, priests and courtiers. On their laps and at their feet, reclined small dogs.

"Who are they?"

"No! Look down at their feet! Look at the dogs…that dog, there." She pointed at one particular animal that bore a striking resemblance to Tai.

"Spanish royalty favored a breed called Beauceron or Lowchen…." Michael recited from the guidebook. Linda didn't hear a word he said she was so totally wrapped up in the painting with the little dog sitting at the Cardinal's feet. Several moments passed before she realized Michael was waiting to continue the tour. Finally she smiled. He welcomed this facial expression.

"Well, that's a relief! Don't tell me we're going to start enjoying our vacation." Before he could touch her, she had moved on.

"'Enjoy' isn't exactly the word I would use to describe the experience I'm having," Linda said as she moved to the next group portrait of royalty and their pets. Several paintings later, she focused on another little black and white dog this time apparently asleep in the church official's lap. The portrait was of a fifty-something man looking down his elegant nose at the servants surrounding his throne. Rather imperiously, his hand was posed as if issuing orders. There was no doubt this was a cleric of formidable power and all the arrogance to go with his persona. Linda lifted her eyes from the sleeping dog to his master. She stared into the cleric's cold hard eyes and an involuntary shudder passed through her body.

"This one looks like Tai, more than the other one – uncanny resemblance," Michael said over her shoulder.

A quick glance back at those eyes and Linda fled the room. Michael had no choice but to follow her down the broad steps and out of the building. As soon as Linda reached the plaza she stopped and turned to wait for Michael to catch up. "I'm sorry, Michael, but I couldn't stay in that building one minute longer. I felt like I was burning up, suffocating....I don't understand it all yet, but I do know it's part of the reason we're here." Tentatively, she smiled up at him. Taking her elbow gently in his hand, he guided her to a small café across the plaza.

After ordering some tea, Michael asked her how she was feeling.

"Better. I still regret leaving Tai at home but some of the worry seems to have receded. I'm no longer afraid. What's on the agenda for tonight?"

"We have terrific seats at a Flamenco performance...."

After a superb meal and fantastic dance performance, they started to stroll back to their hotel. Madrid's narrow cobblestone streets form a maze of confusion particularly after dark when their shadows play tricks on tourists attempting to navigate them with only a Fodor's city map as their guide. After a few false turns, Linda gripped Michael's arm. "Honey, let's find a cab...."

"Why? Are you tired?"

"No, I don't want to get lost...."

"Just this afternoon you were leading me around here as if this were downtown Baltimore...."He stopped to look at her. Another panic attack was coming on. Recognizing the by now familiar fear in her eyes, he turned and flagged down a taxi.

It was Mr. Toad's wild ride! The Spanish taxi lurched into gear passing other cars with only inches to spare, as they careened around corners on two side wheels. The passengers' only defense was to close their eyes and pray.

Suddenly, Linda broke out in a sweat. Her grip on Michael's arm caused him to grunt in pain. Before he could get an explanation a scream of terror passed through her lips. "Stop! Stop the cab now! Ambush!" Blue eyes wide with fright, she pointed at the narrow end of the street. "Up there! Can't you see them?"

"What? Honey, there's no one there…really, no one."

She looked at him in horror and struggled to break free.

"Linda, calm down. Really, there's nothing there, nothing at all to be afraid of, Hon. Believe me."

Her bulbous eyes returned to normal, her breathing slowed down, and the shaking subsided as she said, "You mean you didn't see the mob? The men who were going to attack us…?"

"No, Hon, we didn't see them. But that doesn't mean they weren't there.…"

Glancing at him sharply, she realized he wasn't patronizing her, simply agreeing with her in his gentle matter-of-fact way. Again, she thanked her soul for bringing this man into her life – this soul mate.

Back at the hotel, Linda had not fully recovered from her fright on Madrid's streets. She flipped through the pages of several astrological texts she had brought with her. Searching for answers, or more importantly, searching for questions she knew she needed to ask to clarify this clandestine journey.

At home, Linda had deepened her studies of karmic astrology investigating her past lives along with those of her clients. She was beginning to utilize her love of history to timestamp and translate the symbolic details and clues of past life themes in astrological charts. She was learning the symbolism of countries and the signs that ruled them. She knew her sun sign Sagittarius ruled Spain. She was convinced this trip would answer many questions about her personal karma. Her recent experiences validated this intuitional knowing. She trusted the Socratic process and believed in the value of asking questions – especially when SHE was the seeker of knowledge.

After another restless night, Linda awoke to a chilling dampness that soaked the city streets. Michael made some suggestions of places they could visit. Once more Linda's fear overcame her sense of adventure. She did not want to leave the safety of their room or the comfort of this modern hotel. For the first time in her life, history frightened her instead of grounding her. Finally, she agreed to visit a cathedral in city center. It was one of the sights on Fodor's must-see list, and within easy walking distance.

As they approached the majestic building whose spires reached upward in a futile attempt to touch the kingdom of God, Linda's pace slowed, lagging several steps behind Michael. Realizing she was no longer at his side, he stopped and turned around. It had started again. Linda had a look of pure terror in her eyes. Her hands were shoved deeply into the pockets of her lightweight jacket. Her shoulders were hunched over. Her legs trembled. They entered the cathedral. Her stomach heaved and lurched as her bowels turned to water. She had to find a bathroom immediately. Linda staggered forward into Michael's arms.

"Honey, you look awful! Let's grab a cab and go...."

"No, I'll be all right." She leaned on Michael as he led her to a stone bench nestled into a dark alcove at the side door to the church. By the time they sat down Linda's feet were on fire. Sweat poured from her face and body even though the building's interior temperature could not have been over 50 degrees. "Just let me catch my breath," she pleaded.

All around them groups of tourists were gathered listening to their guides describe the architecture and history of the landmark. Various languages vied for volume control. Taxis honked angrily at each other as they whizzed by outside. Nothing could drown out the bass percussion of her heartbeat.

Satisfied she would be all right for a moment Michael approached the English-speaking guide next to the side door for help.

Linda got up again and began frantically walking around until she found what she was looking for – a large stone. With one fluid movement she bent down picked up the stone and turned to hurl it through the magnificent stained glass window in front of her. Suddenly, a pair of strong hands pinned her arms to her side. In absolute rage she whirled on the man restraining her. "Sudicio! Pig!" Gasping, she realized it was Michael who prevented her from carrying out the destruction to this hallowed ground. Pale, confused, and now very afraid, Michael asked her the obvious question. "Linda? What in the hell do you think you're doing?"

She had no answers. All she remembered was having this compulsion arise to destroy that church and everything associated with it. Still shaken he forced her back to the bench.

The English-speaking guide approached them. "E x c u s e me Senor and Senora, do you need some help?"

"Yes! Yes we do! Could you please tell me what's happened here...in this place," pointing at the marble floor beneath her feet. "I mean in the past, back in history...?"

"Of course. You are in the place of executions. During the Inquisitions the heretics were put to death here. A platform was erected where you are seated from which the Cardinals would pronounce sentence...uh, yes, about where you are sitting now. And the deed would be carried out over there. Are there any other questions I can answer for you?"

Linda was speechless. Michael thanked the guide, gently gathered up his wife and took her back to the hotel. Past lives and what they meant had been an integral part of Linda's studies for years now, but this was the most visceral reaction he had witnessed yet.

All of this was finally making sense. Her burning feet...wait! No, no. It wasn't her feet that had been burning, that was just a fleeting impression…perhaps she was not the victim in this scenario. Perhaps her former experience was as the persecutor.

After a light dinner, Linda fell into another restless sleep. Her mind returned to the picture in the Prado and the Cardinal with his dog on his lap. Then there were flashes of the mob chasing her down the narrow streets. She was moving too fast to be carrying anything. So, where was her dog?

Her eyes snapped open as she burst into tears of shame. That was it! It wasn't her feet that burned it was her beloved dog's. When she had been that Cardinal she had successfully escaped the anger of the crowd yet thought nothing of leaving her precious pet behind. In fact, her only concern had been for herself…saving herself from the righteous rage she had generated by condemning so many people to such horrible deaths! Because the crowd was not able to express their rage on her, they took it out on her dog…the one in the portrait…the one who looked exactly like Tai.

This karmic shame had been carried through many lifetimes in relentless pursuit of Linda's soul to resolve. That dog was the only living thing the priest had ever loved; yet he betrayed it anyway. At last! Now, Linda's exaggerated fears and over-protectiveness for her pets made sense. All were reactions to the guilt she felt but had never forgiven herself for. She prayed to God that the conscious memory of this lifetime held the potential to free her of the shame she'd carried for centuries.

Chapter Twelve

Linda and Michael returned from their trip, which neither of them would ever again refer to as a "vacation" to find Tai in excellent health and overjoyed to see them. Well, happy to welcome Linda back, but apparently not so sure about Michael. Linda resumed her practice with a stronger emphasis on doing the past life work our souls need us to address, resolve and release. She brought the karmic/past life elements into her clients' soul mission discussions and chart interpretations. Michael agreed on the importance of incorporating past life regression work into the practice. His prior hypnosis training and dream analysis work created complementary offerings to Linda's chart interpretations. They made quite a team combining their skill sets. This extra revenue made it possible for them to save for their first home, which they were soon able to afford.

"Damnit Tai! Stop scratching the door!" Michael shouted at the little dog. Tai settled back on his haunches and looked up at Michael towering above him. Michael opened the door, bent down, swept Tai up and brusquely tossed him outside. He landed directly in front of Linda's feet.

"Tai, sweetheart, are you all right?" She scooped him up and glared at Michael. "Was that really necessary?" she said, trying to contain her annoyance.

"I didn't spend days refinishing our new home's woodwork to have your dog ruin it." Michael slammed the door behind them.

Taking a deep breath, Linda decided to calm down before confronting her husband. His behavior toward Tai had become increasingly harsh since their return from Spain. Linda knew something was undermining Michael's desire to connect with Tai – he was too much of an animal lover to be behaving this way. Something else was going on.

Once inside, she placed Tai in his training crate and securely latched the door. "It'll be all right, darling. Mommy's gotta talk to Michael—I'll make him understand how special you are to me...." Or was that the problem? Tai scratched on the gate, wanting to follow, but Linda turned and exited the room.

She found Michael hunched over his guitar working on a new song. He looked up and smiled. But once he got a good look at the expression on her face his smile slid into a tight-lipped smirk. "I know what you're going to say, and I want to stop you right there." Michael had had enough. He'd been feeling demeaned and vindictive and had no intention of keeping these feelings to himself any longer. "Since we brought that dog home, your whole life seems to revolve around him. You want to spend more and more time with him; and you're more affectionate with him than me. What am I, chopped liver?"

His countenance was so telling; he was jealous! Linda felt her anger dissolve into a smile. "Oh, Honey—you don't understand, do you?"

"You're right. I don't understand how a woman can care more about a dog than her own husband! I should never have agreed to let that mutt into my life!" Unconsoled and filled with self-pity, he slammed his guitar into the case and marched out of the house.

Several weeks later, Linda finished teaching her introductory Karmic Astrology class and ushered the last student out of the house. The topic this evening was Soul Creation. She made a bee-line for the kitchen expecting to find Michael there. Until recently she would look forward to conferring with Michael about the students' responses to the new philosophy she was sharing. He provided such a fine sounding board to her more innovative theories. From his scientific viewpoint his "voice of reason" added tremendous depth and contextual bridging to her more spiritual bent. As Linda rinsed the last coffee cup it struck her how much their routine had changed – Michael didn't seem as interested in spending time together these days. A mild flutter of unease moved through her body as she turned out the last light and climbed the stairs.

Michael was already in bed. "Honey, tonight the class was having trouble with the concept of 'our souls creating our lives,'" Linda remarked as she walked into the adjacent bathroom. "They seem unconvinced and unwilling to take responsibility for their lives. There's still so much unconscious projection going on. Some of them are really struggling with the idea that everything and everyone in their lives is of their own creation. One of them wanted to talk about 'why bad things happen to good people,' refusing to admit that there are soul lessons in all that we bring to ourselves." Her voice tailed off as she returned to the bedroom and awaited an answer.

Lying on his stomach, his head turned away from her, Michael's body language indicated his reluctance to participate in the conversation. Moving toward her side of the bed, she picked up a large astrology book from the nightstand and flipped on the light.

"Honey?" Still no response from Michael. Pulling back the covers, Linda slid into bed beside him. Michael cleared his throat. It sounded more like a deep rumble as he began to speak. "Linda, it's time we talked. I have to be honest with you. I...I've had an affair."

Just like that. No lead in, no softening of the blow, just the hard facts. How dare he! White hot heat rose up in her chest. The air rushed into her lungs as she gasped inaudibly, then tears of anger surged into her eyes. Without realizing her strength, she slammed the heavy book right into his shoulder. "You bastard," she hissed. "How could you? Why did you? You lousy, rotten son of a bitch!"

Intent on escaping the fireworks Michael slid from his side of the bed and slithered toward the bedroom entrance. He closed it just before the air-borne book hit the door with a thud. Pausing on the other side, he could hear Linda's muffled sobs before making his way to the couch downstairs.

Linda spent the night vacillating between melodramatic self-indulgence and emotional detachment. Her pride had been seriously wounded. She was in disbelief that her "soul mate" could have betrayed her. Linda allowed the full range of emotions associated with betrayal to pass through her: anger; shame; rage; and sadness; then back to anger again. Her chaotic mind was trying to make some sense of this, as her body reeled with feelings of confusion, fear, and loss.

Oh my God, she thought. Amazing! That's what her class had covered tonight: "Soul Creation" and the importance of gaining perspective and insight on difficult moments in one's life by asking the questions: "Why have I created this situation, and what is the lesson my soul wants me to learn?" All of a sudden it was obvious…she was doing her own soul work now, not merely explaining "how to" to others. Linda took her own advice and asked for help. "Soul, I am ready to open up the door to my unconscious mind. I wish to understand why I would have created this betrayal so it can be resolved. I know you will be with me to guide me and provide the answers I seek." This process she would later call a bi-level conversation. Her intellect framed the questions – her soul provided the answers.

The next morning, on very little sleep, Linda made her way downstairs. She fixed herself a mug of tea and staggered outside to the back porch. There she lowered herself onto the top step of the stairs where she had a branch-high view of their 200 year old maple tree. Tai scurried into her lap when he felt she had finally settled down. Michael's car was gone. He had left for work earlier than usual to avoid the anticipated confrontation.

Linda's soul began to replay the lesson of last night's class. As if punched in the stomach for the second time in 24 hours, Linda asked herself again, "Why has my soul brought this into my life? Why would I set myself up for such pain, and how will this experience contribute to my soul's development?" The process took most of the day, but by nightfall, and with the help of her chart, she had deciphered the answer. Canceling her evening appointments, she put Tai in the car and drove to the hospital where Michael worked. Spotting him in the hallway, she motioned to him to follow her out into the picnic area behind the building.

Seated on the opposite sides of a picnic table with Tai in her lap, she held her hand up when Michael started to speak.

"Linda, I—"

"No, please, let me go first. My soul created this situation to test the sincerity of my belief in the process of Soul Creation. Until tonight it was more of a concept than my felt experience. And Michael, I know my attachment to Tai has been difficult to understand, but he's been teaching me how to love in a way I've never been able to show another human being, until now. I am ready to love you unconditionally, Michael. This is what you wanted from me all along. If I'd been able to provide it, the affair would never have happened. I haven't worked out all the details relative to this event, but I'm certain I will over time. And I'm equally certain our relationship will be stronger for having survived this incident."

Michael's hazel eyes misted and he smiled. "The affair is over, Linda. I promise you that this will never happen again. I have missed you so much. I love you."

This conversation firmly acknowledged her commitment to this man and Michael's need to be accepted for who he was at all times. Six months later Michael and Linda made the decision to get married, trusting their souls to continue to create the growth opportunities their soul-mated relationship was intended to provide.

It was now Indian summer in Baltimore and the triple-digit temperatures were boiling the city with a vengeance one last time before the crisp days of fall set in. Linda poured her coffee and fixed Tai's breakfast. Then she called him several times without a response. Concerned, she climbed up the back staircase to investigate. Tai was curled up in his "cave."

"Tai, baby, come eat breakfast...." Her encouraging words apparently fell on deaf ears. She reached in to pick him up when she distinctly heard him whimper. Linda immediately called for Michael. She carried Tai downstairs to show him his food, but he didn't seem at all interested.

"I'll call the vet," Michael said before Linda could ask.

On the vet's examining table, Tai slumped over only raising his head when he felt the urge to throw up. After a thorough examination, the diagnosis was unclear – they could either leave Tai there for further observation or take him home and watch for additional symptoms. He'd call her later with the results of the blood test if she chose the latter.

It seemed like a very long drive home. Linda held Tai close fearing the worst. Michael empathetically felt her apprehension. He gently reached over, touched her arm, and said what he hoped was the truth. "He'll be all right, Hon. Trust me on that."

The test results were inconclusive but Tai remained "off his feed" for several days. "It's the heat, Hon, it's been affecting everyone, right?" Michael said. "Maybe when the weather breaks he'll improve." The weather finally broke with a display of violent thunder and lightening storms sending Tai scurrying into his cage. One of the lightening strikes threw the whole house into total darkness. After lighting a few candles Michael sat down beside Linda on the couch. "How are you feeling, Hon?"

"Me? Oh, fine…" Linda lied.

"Listen to me. Your color looks really pale, you've been cramping up, and your appetite is as bad as Tai's. I know how much you love him but taking on his symptoms won't make him well, will it?"

She was working something out in her mind by the look on her face. "Perhaps he's mirroring mine…"

Linda stood up and went to her desk to locate her birth chart. As soon as she found it the lights came back on. She grabbed an ephemeris and checked her transits. Her intuition was correct.

The next morning Linda called and scheduled a doctor's appointment with a gastro-intestinal specialist she had seen years ago. Surprisingly Tai's appetite seemed to return the same day.

A week later, Linda was admitted to St. Agnes Hospital. Apparently, her gall bladder had begun to rupture about the same time Tai came down with his mysterious illness. Tai wasn't sick. It was Linda who needed surgery! After he was convinced Linda was out-of-the-woods, Michael returned home to take care of the dog.

Leaning over and unlocking the cave, Michael picked Tai up and affectionately hugged him. Confused and pulling away just a bit, Tai arched his back to look into Michael's eyes.

"I owe you one, buddy. If you hadn't gotten sick when you did our girl would not have gone to see her doc in time to save her life…. Truce?"

Tai relaxed into his arms, as if he completely understood the request. A truce it was!

Chapter Thirteen

The next fifteen years flew by as Linda's practice became internationally recognized and Michael added past-life regression consultations to his already thriving practice. Tai accompanied Linda everywhere – to her classes, counseling sessions and workshops. In 1998, Linda wrote a book with Evan St. Lifer on Karmic Astrology, called *Discovering Your Soul Mission: How to Use Karmic Astrology to Create the Life You Want.* Tai joined her at all her speaking engagements, radio interviews and book signings.

As their reputation grew their repertoire of services expanded to include private retreats. The Brady's built their dream home on 11 acres in Jay, Vermont, and began commuting between there, Baltimore and Florida to accommodate their clients' escalating needs up and down the East Coast. Linda noticed that Tai's talents, as a therapy dog, were most helpful when working in particularly difficult sessions. He used all of his senses to determine which side of his personality to showcase that would best serve Linda's client at hand. He knew how to "get on their wave length" and create a level of relaxation and connection that was remarkable. Soon Linda learned to trust his cues – they actually guided and enhanced her own intuitional abilities through rather unorthodox methods. The two of them made a great counseling team while they simultaneously fulfilled their soul mission.

As signs of Tai's aging became more apparent Linda began to anticipate and fear her reaction to his inevitable passing. She had learned so much from their relationship. Nevertheless her mind appeared to be more accepting of this concept than her heart, which still found the approaching separation unbearable.

At this point in his life, arthritic and deaf, Tai had to be carried outside to go to the bathroom. Linda hand fed him to encourage him to eat. Michael cradled him gently whenever it was time for Tai to come to bed. Wherever they went Linda and Michael made sure he had the best seat in the house. Tai's baby sitters loved him as well. He saw an acupuncturist regularly. Linda's students even practiced Reiki and other holistic therapies on Tai to ease his discomfort. She communicated with him regularly through meditation and performed daily auric brush-downs on him herself. In spite of the success achieved in slowing his aging process, the approaching end to Tai's life was imminent.

Her voice shook as she watched him sleep. "Michael, when will it be time to help him pass over?"

Michael lowered his newspaper, paused and tenderly responded, "He will let us know."

"I believe that, but will his awareness of my fear over ride his desire to escape his own pain?"

The rustle of the newspaper collapsing in Michael's lap drew Linda's attention to her husband. He peered over the front page and looked directly at his wife. "Linda, you are incapable of allowing your pet to suffer...trust in that."

Each night, before putting him to sleep, she held Tai to her chest and begged him for a sign when he was ready to pass over and return home to Arabeth. Immediately, he would fall fast to sleep. Linda knew he was sleeping a great deal now in order to spend time on the other side – a kind and graceful way to ease the transition whenever it came.

Only days later, Linda went to get Tai for breakfast. She rushed to his cave-bed. One side of his body was limp, the other stiff. Immediately she called the vet who suspected a stroke. He asked Linda to bring him in as soon as possible. With tears streaming down her face Linda carried Tai to the car.

By the time they arrived at the vet's office Tai had rallied somewhat. Linda watched as the vet examined him on the shiny silver table. Quietly sobbing Linda damned herself for her selfish lack of faith. She knew what to expect, she knew it was in the master plan, she knew she had created it for her own good – but why did it have to hurt so much?

She felt the vet's gentle touch. "We can send him on his way any time now...."

"No! He's not ready. I know he's not ready...."

"He's not ready, or you're not ready to release him?" The vet's question pierced her heart.

Through watery, blurred eyes, Linda stared through the vet's wire rimmed glasses and drew a deep breath "Thank you, but I know he is not ready now. I will know when he is...."

As soon as she uttered those words she recognized them as the truth.

Only a few days later Tai stumbled then tumbled, down the front steps. Linda rushed down after him and turned him over as gently as she knew how. "Tai my little one, are you all right?" She smiled down at him. He shifted his stare to look directly into her eyes. He spoke volumes to her with just that look. It was time. He had survived the fall physically but spiritually he had made the decision to move on. "You are ready now, aren't you, Tai?"

Linda promised herself she would honor his request. The rest of that day and evening Linda spent holding Tai, each communicating their love for each other heart to heart. The process provided emotional comfort for Linda as it provided physical comfort for Tai. They were equally resolved and committed to their soul contract. And, for the first time in her life, Linda found peace in her heart and attained a serene place of benign detachment in her soul.

Michael and she had previously scheduled a book signing in New York City for the following day. As she spoke to the group her tears flowed freely when she expressed her belief in soul contracts between animals and their owners. Tai and Linda had shared a commitment through multiple reincarnations, to learn the karmic lessons needed to further evolve their souls. And the most rewarding lesson of all was to learn to live in unconditional love.

Her voice shook at first, but gathered strength as the power of her message supported her. Yes, tomorrow was the day Tai would die, his body would cease to live, but his soul would transform into the next spiritual stage. And soon, a healthier, happier Tai would return to her when he was ready. In this lifetime he had fulfilled his contract with Linda, and his life had become a valuable lesson to all who attended the book signing.

The audience was observably moved. They shared her grief and many shared her conviction that animals, in fact, do have souls and those souls are intricately associated with ours now, and forever.

I knew when Linda made the decision to release my body. I am grateful that she loves me enough to let me go. We spent the whole night awake and together. She told me she would love me forever. Lying on her heart I assured her I would be back very soon. I could feel it – her heart was totally open! I am so proud. I have successfully completed my mission. I have earned the gift of spiritual freedom and am ready to go home to my spiritual teacher, Arabeth.

Linda's speech in New York City became my eulogy. She was so miserable and didn't want to talk at all, but knew she must share what she had lived and learned. She talked about our soul contract. Through her tears she told the people that somehow she would find the strength and selflessness to put me down the next day. She knew I would go to the other side and return to her soon. During that talk she wept uncontrollably at times, and so did her audience. Everyone in the room felt the truth of how deeply animal soul connections touch peoples' lives and how my love and patience had changed her life.

On the ride home Linda had a dream about Arabeth. In it Arabeth told Linda that she needed to write a story about our soul journey together. People would learn that animals have souls too. It would comfort pet owners and help them feel less pain when it was time for their animal's soul to depart. The book would explain that animals' relatively short lives create many opportunities for humans to: observe and revere the cycle of life; face loss with compassion for themselves; learn the importance of grieving and how it can eliminate ongoing suffering if processed fully; and to FEEL the incredible joy and connectedness that love can bring into one's life when it's given unconditionally. And, lastly, that the soul contracts they have with their pets need to be honored.

That fateful day arrived. Linda prepared Tai for his long journey, then jangled her car keys in a signal to Michael that it was time to go. Her heart tightened in a knot that restricted the blood flow to every muscle in her body, if only for a moment. She closed her eyes, took a very deep breath, and reminded herself that this is what a pet owner does for their beloved animal when they ask to be released. This selfless act allows pets to transform into spirit once again, regenerate their bodies and prepare for their return. Michael entered the room, took the keys from her hand and without a word kissed her tenderly on the top of her head. Linda whimpered as she relinquished her Tai into her husband's hands. There was no need for her to go with them; she had already said her "goodbyes."

Within the hour Linda felt a cramping in her chest. She knew the moment Tai had passed. The void was so overwhelming it caused her to gasp for air...she wondered if this is what a heart attack felt like. Pulling herself to her feet, she staggered toward the door to the garden in the front yard. Beneath the maple tree stood Tai's favorite statue of a young maiden holding a sheaf of wheat. Linda watched the street for a sign of Michael's car when she caught a wisp of spirit in her peripheral vision. It was Arabeth with Tai! They paused next to the statue then were gone. But Arabeth's voice lingered with a message.

"Tai is fine now and will be ready to return soon. Do not fret, dear one, you did well. God is proud of you both."

Leaning against the doorframe, Linda waited and whispered "There will be no more goodbyes, Tai. I will see you soon." She had no idea how much time passed before she heard the sound of a car pull up in front of the house.

It is done. I have left my body. I paused in our garden by the little girl holding wheat. Linda came onto the front porch. She saw me! I want to leave quickly, but I know I need to stay for awhile. I watch Linda very closely. She is broken hearted, but it's different than the last time... She knows that her pain will not kill her. She knows that I will be back. She knows that if she allows herself to mourn and FEEL her sadness it will lead her back to the joy, laughter, and intimacy we shared. And when she closes her eyes she will know I am not gone forever, whenever she hears my footfall in her heart.

Michael's heavy steps approached her, as she stood at the door. Turning, she fell into her grief stricken husband's arms and they cried together as if their hearts would break.

At Arabeth's side, Tai saw Michael return. He watched them sob together, then glanced up at Arabeth. "It is part of what they need to do to heal," she said. Tai knew this, and believed it. Yet no matter how many lifetimes he'd witnessed it, it didn't seem to get any easier. Then Tai sent this message to their hearts. "Open your hearts and you will hear me…I am free; happy and healthy."

Suddenly their tears formed into smiles. "Tai is free of pain again. Tai is whole again. He left us his love to help us with his transition." His Leo ascendant showed itself at every opportunity – even this one. Charming, arrogant, funny… dear Tai….lovely, loving Tai.

"I watched Linda and Michael as they experienced the pain and agony of losing their precious Tai. I felt their hearts breaking from the sadness. I listened to Linda when she told Michael to stay with his pain as she was feeling her own. They intuitively knew that staying in their hearts would open up a new space… a space for joy and freedom. Linda and Michael's hearts were breaking, not just out of grief and pain, but in a quest to break open to experience more of life and themselves. Tai's spirit was free now and he was joyful and they could feel him! That was bliss! Their opened hearts were able to receive and feel his happiness. Intensity of pain transformed into total joy in seconds. There would be grief, of course, but knowing that their Tai would heal and return, would alter that too."

126

The next day brought sunshine. "Michael," Linda cried. "Tai and Arabeth came to me again last night in a dream. He is with her and he is healthy. He seems so happy to be able to return home. My God, he feels so light, no pain, just so joyful. It is like he's actually talking to me—here." Linda pointed to her heart, then reached over and placed her hand on Michael's heart. "Here, do you feel Tai in your heart?"

Michael smiled and nodded. "He's coming back soon, isn't he?"

Tai's message: "Tell the people who have lost their animals to wait for the joy...."

Epilogue

Linda knew Tai II had returned because her heart was heavy again and she missed him terribly. She had experienced so much joy when Tai I was spirit. Now she knew that he had returned to earth and she had to find him.

She found him on Easter Sunday of 1999 in the *Baltimore Sun*. She saw the ad and called the number at 8:30 in the morning, apologizing profusely for the early hour on this resurrection morning. Her words stumbled out, "I know this might sound strange to you, but I know my pet Shih Tzu has returned to earth and he might be there among your litter pups. Please, I need to know; can I come and meet the puppies now?"

"Yes, of course." The woman willingly agreed. She was a spiritual woman who loved animals too.

An hour later Linda and Michael walked into a house south of Baltimore City. They waited while the woman brought out four Shih Tzu puppies and placed them in a playpen in the middle of the living room. Linda sat down on the floor and asked the woman if she would let them out of the playpen. As the breeder opened the gate all fur and fun tumbled onto the floor. Linda sat back, closed her eyes and said to Tai I's soul: "Tai, if you are here, please come to me. Connect to my heart the way you used to." It was a silent prayer that she knew only Tai's soul would hear. She waited. One pup came to her but quickly walked away. Then another and then finally, this one little pup came from nowhere, bounded into Linda's arms and snuggled into her body, heart to heart.

"Welcome home, little one. Remember I promised you there would be No More Goodbyes...."

Appendix

A Message from Linda Brady:

Tai has been an integral part of my soul's journey over lifetimes. His soul has comforted me and opened my heart, yet it's also been the source of my greatest pain. He taught me about my past. He showed me my capacity for love and compassion as well as brought to my attention times when I displayed flagrant disregard and disrespect for myself and others. He has served my mind, body and my spirit. I love and honor him beyond words.

This book is dedicated to this courageous soul that has chosen to be a part of my life's journey. I have grown because of him and for him. I thank him from the bottom of my heart, which he has worked so hard to open.

Tai is one of my most significant soul mates. He is here to help me answer the most important questions of my life. Every day, he teaches me to open my heart and love unconditionally. He helps me understand that being able to feel pain and sadness means that I can also experience joy. He shows me how important it is to share my grief with others, and in the sharing, heal them and myself.

He teaches me how transformation occurs when I have the courage to allow change into my life. Throughout our relationship his presence is a gentle reminder of how serendipity brings its many blessings to me. I honor the importance of living in the present to be able to count my perfect moments. Yet when I forget this precious truth, Tai somehow knows this and does something to bring me back to the moment.

The following techniques have been invaluable in my journey with Tai's soul. I hope that they will help you with your soul mates too.

DAILY SERENITY MEDITATION
FOR USE WHEN:
- You know that you need to embrace the present and its serenity
- You or your pet are feeling overwhelmed with life and its pressures
- You or your pet are feeling worried and anxious

Create a special time and place for you and your pet. Make a commitment to spending quiet time with them daily - a few minutes is all that you need. Begin the meditation by stroking their fur. As you are doing that you are feeling the color yellow forming over the top of your head. Allow that color to come into your body, warming and loving you. Let that color move throughout your body into your right hand. Send that into the body of your pet.

Your pet will return it to you very naturally. You have created a circle of yellow that moves from you to your pet and back to you. Speak the following words out loud to your pet and yourself: "As this color moves from me to you, we are feeling more and more relaxed and serene with energy that is true." You will notice that you are totally in the moment and that all is well. You and your pet are centered and aligned in this precious experience.

HEART CENTER MEDITATION
FOR USE WHEN:

- You are feeling disconnected and lonely
- You are feeling sad
- You feel tension or tightness in your heart

Go to your special place with your pet. Sit in a way that your heart and theirs are in perfect alignment. Feel your hearts connecting. Feel the warmth that is extending from you to them and back. Draw this energy deep into your heart. As you are doing this, you are feeling the color green forming over the top of your head. Allow that color to come into your body, warming and loving your heart. Let that color move throughout your body into your right hand. Send that into the heart of your pet. Your pet will return it to you very naturally. You have created a circle of green that moves from your heart to the heart of your pet and back. Speak the following words out loud to your pet and yourself: "Thank you for your loving open heart. My heart center opens because of you. We are connected in love and trust."

CLEANSING MEDITATION

Animals have natural empathy and may experience emotional and physical illness from being around intense feelings and illness. Service dogs, therapy dogs, and police dogs are especially vulnerable and need to have their auras treated several times a day.

Cleaning their energetic field (which is called the aura) is the most important habit that we can create with our pets. Dogs especially are being used more and more in service roles — which put them at emotional and psychic risk. Doing this exercise, even if it is once a week is essential for their health. I know that Tai lived as long as he did, in good health, because of this psychic routine.

FOR USE WHEN:

- Your pet has been exposed to intense emotions such as anger, sadness or fear
- Your pet has been around illness
- Your pet has experienced any type of change in their daily routine
- Your pet has been ill
- Your pet has been to the Vet

Go to your special place with your pet. Begin the process by centering yourself and breathing in good positive energy from the Universe. Feel the color purple over your head. Allow it into your body, filling your body with love and protection. When you feel filled up, you are going to create a bubble of protection around your body from your head to your feet. Now you are energetically protected to do a "brush down" on your pet. Run your left hand over your pet's body, about 8 inches above their physical body. Close your eyes and feel your pet's energy. This will take practice and sooner or later you will feel heat emanating from your pet's auric field. Pay attention to the feelings that you have in your heart. You may notice that your pet's energy feels a little intense, anxious or "off." As you move your hand over your pet's body, begin to "pull" this energy away from its body. When you pull it out, throw it away (being careful that the energy is not thrown at a person, plant or animal). Make sure that you are not absorbing this energy. (This is why you have created an auric bubble around yourself.) Continue pulling and throwing this problematic energy until your pet's energy feels even and peaceful. When this occurs take a moment and with your right hand, send your pet a color that you feel will help it from absorbing negative energy. I like strong colors, like purple, green or orange, for this, but you will know what will work. Speak the following words out loud to your pet: "Energy that is not in your best interest will not penetrate this field." Use this especially if the pet is going to be exposed to more intensity and negative energy.

SOUL CONVERSATIONS

I am in constant communication with my soul and with the soul of my pets. I talk to my pets' souls, and my soul, plus we have soul-to-soul talks. There is a lot of talking going on every day. Often the conversations are about daily things. I know that my pets' souls love being in Vermont. They love playing in the snow in winter, in the leaves in the fall and in the brook in the summer. I laugh with their souls when they are so filled with puppy joy in this earthly experience. I speak to their souls when their doggie personalities are being stubborn, asking for a little help in their training. I know that my pets' souls are interested in doing their own soul mission. I will remind my pets of this occasionally. I see my pets' souls often playing with mine and revel in this wonder. To have established this level of communication makes it easier when life's challenges occur.

The day that Tai passed we had a soul to soul talk. We went to our special place and sat with his heart next to mine. His was very weak, so I sent him some of my heart energy. This is the conversation my soul had with his personality: "Today we are going to release your soul. Arabeth is waiting to take you home, my dear precious soul. I love you with all of my heart and will love you forever. Our work here on earth is not done, so you are going to return to us quickly. Listen carefully to your teacher, so that you will be ready." His soul smiled. My personality cried, and it was done. I handed my precious Tai to Michael to take to his appointment with Arabeth.

Bibliography

Brady, Linda and St. Lifer, Evan. *Discovering Your Soul Mission: How to Use Karmic Astrology To Create the Life You Want.* Three Rivers Press, 1998.

Clow, Barbara Hand. *Liquid Light of Sex: Kundalini Rising at Mid-life Crisis.* Bears & Company, 1996.

Green, Liz. *Saturn: A New Look at an Old Devil.* Samuel Weiser, 1976.

Schulman, Martin. Karmic *Astrology: The Moon Nodes.* Samuel Weiser, 1975.